INDIANS

BLACK HAWK, *Cleven*
OSCEOLA, *Clark*
POCAHONTAS, *Seymour*
PONTIAC, *Peckham*
SACAGAWEA, *Seymour*
SEQUOYAH, *Snow*
SITTING BULL, *Stevenson*
SQUANTO, *Stevenson*
TECUMSEH, *Stevenson*

NAVAL HEROES

DAVID FARRAGUT, *Long*
GEORGE DEWEY, *Long*
JOHN PAUL JONES, *Snow*
MATTHEW CALBRAITH PERRY, *Scharbach*
OLIVER HAZARD PERRY, *Long*
RAPHAEL SEMMES, *Snow*
STEPHEN DECATUR, *Smith*

NOTED WIVES and MOTHERS

ABIGAIL ADAMS, *Wagoner*
DOLLY MADISON, *Monsell*
ELEANOR ROOSEVELT, *Weil*
JESSIE FREMONT, *Wagoner*
MARTHA WASHINGTON, *Wagoner*
MARY TODD LINCOLN, *Wilkie*
NANCY HANKS, *Stevenson*
RACHEL JACKSON, *Govan*

SCIENTISTS and INVENTORS

ABNER DOUBLEDAY, *Dunham*
ALBERT EINSTEIN, *Hammontree*
ALECK BELL, *Widdemer*
CYRUS McCORMICK, *Dobler*
ELI WHITNEY, *Snow*
ELIAS HOWE, *Corcoran*
ELIZABETH BLACKWELL, *Henry*
GAIL BORDEN, *Paradis*
GEORGE CARVER, *Stevenson*
GEORGE EASTMAN, *Henry*
GEORGE PULLMAN, *Myers*
GEORGE WESTINGHOUSE, *Dunham*
HENRY FORD, *Aird and Ruddiman*
JOHN AUDUBON, *Mason*
JOHN BURROUGHS, *Frisbee*
JOHN DEERE, *Bare*
JOHN FITCH, *Stevenson*
LEE DeFOREST, *Dobler*
LUTHER BURBANK, *Burt*
MARIA MITCHELL, *Melin*
ROBERT FULTON, *Henry*
ROBERT GODDARD, *Moore*

SAMUEL MO... ...RIGHT, ...O,

CIVIC LEADERS

BETSY ROSS, *Weil*
BOOKER T. WASHINGTON, *Stevenson*
CLARA BARTON, *Stevenson*
DAN BEARD, *Mason*
DOROTHEA DIX, *Melin*
FRANCES WILLARD, *Mason*
J. STERLING MORTON, *Moore*
JANE ADDAMS, *Wagoner*
JOHN PETER ZENGER, *Long*
JULIA WARD HOWE, *Wagoner*
JULIETTE LOW, *Higgins*
LILIUOKALANI, *Newman*
LUCRETIA MOTT, *Burnett*
MOLLY PITCHER, *Stevenson*
OLIVER WENDELL HOLMES, JR., *Dunham*
SUSAN ANTHONY, *Monsell*

SOLDIERS

ANTHONY WAYNE, *Stevenson*
BEDFORD FORREST, *Parks*
DAN MORGAN, *Bryant*
DOUGLAS MacARTHUR, *Long*
ETHAN ALLEN, *Winders*
FRANCIS MARION, *Steele*
GEORGE CUSTER, *Stevenson*
ISRAEL PUTNAM, *Stevenson*
JEB STUART, *Winders*
NATHANAEL GREENE, *Peckham*
ROBERT E. LEE, *Monsell*
SAM HOUSTON, *Stevenson*
TOM JACKSON, *Monsell*
U. S. GRANT, *Stevenson*
WILLIAM HENRY HARRISON, *Peckham*
ZACK TAYLOR, *Wilkie*

STATESMEN

ABE LINCOLN, *Stevenson*
ANDY JACKSON, *Stevenson*
DAN WEBSTER, *Smith*
FRANKLIN ROOSEVELT, *Weil*
HENRY CLAY, *Monsell*
HERBERT HOOVER, *Comfort*
JAMES MONROE, *Widdemer*
JEFF DAVIS, *de Grummond and Delaune*
JOHN F. KENNEDY, *Frisbee*
JOHN MARSHALL, *Monsell*
TEDDY ROOSEVELT, *Parks*
WOODROW WILSON, *Monsell*

Harvey S. Firestone

Young Rubber Pioneer

Illustrated by Fred M. Irvin

Harvey S. Firestone

Young Rubber Pioneer

By Adrian Paradis

 THE BOBBS-MERRILL COMPANY, INC.
A SUBSIDIARY OF HOWARD W. SAMS & CO., INC.
Publishers • INDIANAPOLIS • NEW YORK

LIBRARY OF CONGRESS CATALOG CARD NUMBER: 68-17023

PRINTED IN THE UNITED STATES OF AMERICA

For Andrea and Ian

Illustrations

Full pages

Numerous smaller illustrations

Contents

Books by Adrian Paradis

GAIL BORDEN: RESOURCEFUL BOY
HARVEY S. FIRESTONE: YOUNG RUBBER PIONEER

★ ★ Harvey S. Firestone

Young Rubber Pioneer

Learning A Lesson

"Whoa, Jennifer! Whoa!" Harvey Firestone was sitting on the front seat of the wagon with his friend George Cole. They were making believe that Jennifer, the family horse, was pulling them around the yard.

"My turn to drive," George said.

"That's right," Harvey agreed, and they changed places. Unlike George, who was chubby, Harvey was short and thin for a five-year-old boy. Although he was shy, he liked to have fun and was a happy youngster.

"Where shall we drive now?" George asked. "Down to the railroad?"

"Yes, we'll meet Grandmother Flickinger," Harvey said. "She's coming home——"

"Harvey! Harvey!" Mrs. Firestone called. "Come here, please. I need you."

"Coming, Mother." Harvey jumped down from the wagon. "I'll be right back," he told his friend as he started toward the house. King, the Firestones' collie, followed him.

Harvey's home was a large brick house, built in 1828, one of the first of its kind to be erected in Ohio. It was about five miles from Columbiana, a town south of Akron and near the Pennsylvania border.

Harvey's grandfather and great-grandfather had made the bricks and cut the wood that had been used in making the house. It was shaded by large trees. When the family sat on the porch they could look beyond the road over the gently rolling fields.

"I think I know what you want," Harvey said

as soon as he saw the little tin pail his mother was holding. "Cookies for Mrs. Cole?"

"That's right," Mrs. Firestone said and she smiled. She was a tall, good-looking woman who wore her black hair parted in the middle.

"Mrs. Cole is sick again," she said. "Maybe these will help cheer her up." She lifted the lid and took out two dark brown molasses cookies. As she held them out toward the boys she winked. "Here are a couple of samples. See if they are all right, will you?"

Harvey took them and thanked his mother.

"I'd take these over myself," Mrs. Firestone added, "but I can't leave Robert alone. He is taking his nap." Robert was Harvey's year-old brother. Besides Harvey, the middle son, there was Elmer, ten years old, who was at school.

"Be sure to keep the lid on," Mrs. Firestone warned, "and tell Mrs. Cole there's no hurry returning the pail." She looked down at her small son. "Be careful. Go straight down there and come right home. Do you understand?"

"Yes, Mother."

Harvey took the pail and returned to the wagon. King followed again.

"Here's a cookie for you, George," Harvey said. "Those in the pail are for your mother. I have to take them to her."

"Good!" George said. "Then I can show you my turtle."

Munching their cookies, the boys started for the Cole farm. It was about a mile away, across the rolling pastures that lay behind the Firestones' large white barn. As the boys walked past the barn Harvey heard a horse neigh.

"That must be Jennifer," he said.

There was another neigh.

"How can you tell?" George asked.

"Oh, I know," Harvey assured him. "Each of our horses makes a different noise." He told

14

George how Jennifer had hurt her foot when she slipped in the mud on the way home from church. "Let's give her one of your mother's cookies and say hello," he suggested.

"All right," George agreed. "I know that she'd like Jennifer to have one."

"You know what?" Harvey asked, as they came to the barn.

"No, what?"

"My father said he would give me a great big surprise when I'm older. I don't know what it is and Father won't tell me."

"Do you think it might be a snake or a frog or a rabbit?" George asked. He was very fond of animals.

"Maybe, but a frog isn't very big," Harvey replied. "I wish I knew."

What he really wanted was Pinto, the black pony. Harvey was sure, though, that his father would not give him a pony.

King pushed his way ahead of them and through the barn door. It was cool and dark inside. Harvey liked the smell of the fresh grass that had just been piled in the lofts.

It was hard to see at first, but in a moment the boys became used to the darkness. There was another neigh from the stall on the far side of the building, followed by the stamping of a heavy foot.

"It's us," Harvey called, afraid that they had frightened the horse. "George is here, too."

"So is King," George shouted.

Jennifer was looking out over the door of the stall.

"How's your leg?" Harvey asked. "Father says it's getting better." Jennifer was Mr. Firestone's favorite horse. He always chose her to pull the buggy to church on Sunday.

"She looks all right to me," George said, "but maybe she could use a cookie."

Harvey put the tin pail on the floor and removed the lid. Then he took out the largest cookie he could find.

"Here, Jennifer," he said. Standing on his tiptoes he held the cookie as high as he could. Jennifer leaned her head down, sniffed, and grabbed it.

"She almost ate my hand, too!" Harvey said as he pulled his arm back quickly. The boys stood and watched as the horse chewed the cookie and then sought another.

"That's all," Harvey said. "We've got to go now." He turned around to pick up the pail and let out a shriek. "King!"

"What's wrong?" George asked.

"King's eaten up all the cookies!"

While the boys were feeding Jennifer, King had gobbled the cookies.

"Look!" Harvey said. "King knocked the pail over to get them. Oh, you bad dog!"

King knew that he had done something
wrong. He walked slowly over to the far end
of the barn where he stood and then turned
around to look back at the boys.

18

"What will I do now?" Harvey asked. "Mother will be very angry."

"You don't have to tell her," George suggested. "She'll never know."

Harvey thought about this idea.

"No, I couldn't do that," he said, shaking his head. "It isn't true."

If only they had not stopped in the barn! If only they had not given Jennifer a cookie! If only King had not eaten the cookies! But there was no way to change what had happened and it was all Harvey's fault.

"I'll go tell her," Harvey said as he picked up the pail and put the lid on it again.

I'll come, too," George said. "Do you think she'll give you a licking?"

"No, but my father will give me an extra chore to do," Harvey replied.

The boys walked slowly back to the house. King followed at a distance, his tail between his legs. Mrs. Firestone, who was working in the kitchen, looked out the window and saw the boys coming. She went to the door.

"Why, Harvey!" she exclaimed. "How did you ever get there and back so quickly?"

He hung his head. "I didn't."

"You didn't? What happened?"

"It was all King's fault." Harvey told her what had happened and how King had eaten up all the brown cookies.

Mrs. Firestone could not help smiling, although she was annoyed, too.

"Oh, that dog!" she said. "What will he do next?" Then she looked cross. "But you shouldn't have given Jennifer cookies which were for Mrs. Cole, should you?"

Harvey shook his head.

"I'm glad you were truthful, though, and I always want you to tell the truth. Bring the pail in and I'll fill it again."

The boys went into the kitchen and Mrs. Firestone filled the pail with cookies a second time. "Now George can take them home to his mother," she said, giving him the pail. "You'll go right home, won't you?"

George nodded. "Yes, Mrs. Firestone," he said and ran out the door.

"Hereafter I expect you to do as you are told," Mrs. Firestone told Harvey. "If you had gone directly to Mrs. Cole's this would not have happened. Now go tell your father about it."

Mr. Firestone was in the barn feeding one of the baby lambs. He was a short man who had chin whiskers and a kind face. He did not talk a great deal but did a lot of thinking. He never laughed out loud, but when something was funny he chuckled to himself.

"Mother sent me here," Harvey said.

There was a pause. Then Mr. Firestone asked, "Well, what is it this time, son?"

Harvey told him what had happened. When he finished, his father thought for a moment, then asked, "Did you learn a lesson?"

Harvey nodded.

"All right," Mr. Firestone continued, "as long as you have learned a lesson, that is good. You will never do it again?"

Harvey hung his head and nodded.

"You know that I do not like to punish you," Mr. Firestone said. "But it is the only way to make you remember to be good. Now let's see. First you can sweep out the stalls, then feed the cows, and then—" he paused as a slight smile played about his mouth—" you may have a short ride on the pony."

"Ride the pony!" Harvey exclaimed. "Oh, thank you, Father!"

He ran to do the extra chores. Tonight he would ask about the surprise. Maybe Father would tell him something.

22

The Open Gate

HARVEY and George Cole were playing in the hayloft of the barn. It was just about a year after King had eaten the cookies. Harvey still did not know what the surprise would be. His father promised to give it to him sometime when he did not expect it.

"Watch me swing!" George called to Harvey. He grabbed the end of a rope that hung from the roof and ran a few steps. Then he jumped up and let the rope carry him high in the air. He let go and fell into the deep sweet-smelling hay.

"My turn!" Harvey said as the rope came

swinging back towards him. He ran with the rope, pulled himself up and sailed out far above the hay. When he finally let go he landed way beyond George.

"That was fun!" George said as he brushed the hay off his clothes. "Let's do it again and this time——"

"Harvey! Harvey! Where are you? Chore time!" a voice called from below. "Better do your chores now before the folks come home."

It was Elmer, Harvey's brother. Elmer's chore was to milk the three cows. Mr. Firestone kept just enough cows to provide the family with milk, cream, and butter. He made most of his money raising sheep and growing wheat.

"All right. I'm coming," Harvey answered.

Turning to George he said, "I'll have to go now and take care of the chickens."

This was Harvey's chore. Every morning and evening he took them water and feed. In the morning he also hunted for eggs. He carried them in to his mother in a little basket she had given him.

"I'll help with your chores," George said. "I like chickens. I wish my father would let me feed ours."

"You may feed them tonight," Harvey said, glad to have help. "I'll fill their water pans and you can give them the corn. Race you to the chicken yard."

The boys ran to the fence that kept the chickens inside their own yard. In the middle of the yard stood a low coop where the chickens slept and stayed during bad weather. Harvey opened the gate for George and let him walk in ahead of him.

"Shoo—shoo!" he said to a rooster that tried to get through the opening.

Harvey looked in the coop. "There's no feed here," he said. "We'll have to get some from the barn. I'll show you where it is, George, and then I'll get the water."

They returned to the barn and filled a pail with corn. George started for the chicken yard while Harvey went to the house to get a bucket of water. He was almost there when he heard George call, "Harvey! Come quickly! The chickens—they got out of the yard."

Harvey ran back as fast as he could. Sure enough, the gate was open and most of the chickens were outside their yard. This had happened once before, but only a few hens had gone out and Harvey's father had put them back inside. Today Mr. Firestone wasn't home to help.

"Shoo them back!" Harvey cried.

The boys tried scaring the chickens through the gate. Instead of going into the yard they ran in every direction. Now they were even farther away from the gate.

"Let's carry them back," Harvey suggested as he grabbed a small hen and held it close to him. It jumped about in his arms and made a loud clucking noise. Then it flapped its wings and got away.

George was trying to hold on to a large rooster. It was making a terrible noise and started to peck George's arm. George let go. "That won't work," he said. "We'll have to do something else. I think that maybe Elmer will help."

"He can't leave the milking," Harvey said. "We'll have to do it ourselves, like this."

He reached down, picked up a chicken and held it upside down by its legs. This time he reached the gate and put the chicken inside. George tried to do the same, but the hen beat its wings so hard he had to let it go.

"We've got to think of something else," Harvey said. He was scared. What would he do

if all the chickens got away? He knew how important they were for food. Besides, his mother was very proud of her chicken dinners. She enjoyed serving them to friends who came to the farm for one of her tasty meals.

"I'll get Hiram to help," Harvey said. "I'll be right back."

He found the hired man behind the barn, washing his hands and face. Hiram was a large man with a red moustache. His face and arms were tanned from working in the fields.

"Hiram, the chickens got out of the yard. Please help us get them in," Harvey said.

The hired man splashed more water on his face, then shook his head.

"Get them yourself," he said. "You let them out. You can get them in. I'm through working for today."

"But we can't make them go back in," Harvey said. "Please come."

"You heard me," Hiram said. "Now scat and get them in yourself. And next time remember to close the gate."

Harvey wanted to ask Elmer for help, but he knew that his brother would only laugh at him. Besides, when he was milking he did not want anyone to bother him.

Harvey ran back to George and the chickens. He did not know what to do.

"I've got an idea!" George said. "Open the gate. Then you and I will walk together and shoo them back into the yard."

"Good!" Harvey said, glad to try anything that might get the hens and roosters back where they belonged.

The boys held hands and shooed the chickens ahead of them. A few went back into the yard, but before George could close the gate, most of them had come out again.

"Hey! Get away from there!" Harvey yelled

at two roosters that were eating corn from the pail. He picked up the pail and as he walked with it the roosters followed him. Suddenly he knew what to do.

"I know how to get them in!" he called to George. "If I drop corn on the ground they'll eat it and follow me."

"What are you talking about?" George asked. "I'm tired. I'm going home."

"Wait, George! Don't go yet," Harvey said. "Now watch."

He threw a little corn on the ground near some chickens that were looking for food. At once they ran over and gobbled up the kernels. Then he threw a little more corn close to the gate. The chickens rushed over to eat it, too. Each time he threw corn the chickens moved closer to the yard. Soon the other chickens saw what was happening and came running over to eat the corn, too.

"You wait beside the gate," Harvey told George. "When they're all in, shut it."

He kept throwing corn. The chickens were so hungry that they did not notice where they were going. They even pushed their way through the gate to get the food. When the last one was inside, George slammed the gate shut.

"Hurray! It worked!" Harvey shouted. "I'll never leave that old gate open again."

"And you can have your old chickens," George said as he carefully let himself out through the gate. "I'm going home."

Harvey put the rest of the corn in the feeder and went back to the house for the water. Each time he opened the gate he made certain that he closed it tightly behind him.

That evening as usual Hiram was the first to finish his dinner. As he pushed his chair back from the table he looked at Harvey and asked, "Did you get all those chickens back in the

32

yard again?" Then he left the room before Harvey could answer.

All eyes turned toward Harvey.

"What's this?" Mr. Firestone said.

Harvey scratched his ear and made a face. Then he told what had happened and how he got the chickens back into their yard.

Mr. Firestone, who had listened carefully, chuckled. He pushed his chair back from the table and stared at the ceiling for a moment before he spoke.

"Harvey," he said at last, "I'm very proud of you. You stuck to the job even though at first you couldn't get the chickens back. Just as important, you used your head. I like people who can think. A man who uses his brains gets ahead in this world."

Harvey's face became very red. It was nice to hear his father say such good things about him, but it embarrassed him when Mr. Firestone said them in front of the other members of the family.

"I think," Mr. Firestone continued, "that now is a good time to give you your surprise." He looked across at Harvey and winked. "Would you agree to that?"

Harvey was so excited he hardly knew what his father was saying.

"What is it, Father?" he asked eagerly. "What can it be?"

"What would you like most of all?" Mr. Firestone asked.

Harvey did not know whether or not he should tell his father. There was only one thing in all the world he wanted, and he did not really think his father would give him *that*.

Before he knew what he was doing, he jumped from his chair, ran to his father's side, and almost shouted, "Pinto the pony!"

Mr. Firestone chuckled.

"Really?" He pretended to be surprised. "Well, then, that is exactly what the surprise shall be!"

Without even waiting to thank his father, Harvey skipped as fast as he could to the barn. It was very dark inside the building, but he knew his way. He found the pony quickly. Then he patted Pinto and rubbed his mane.

"You're mine—all mine!" he said. "Oh, Pinto, just think of that! We'll have lots of fun together, won't we?"

Then he ran back to the house. He remembered that he had not thanked his father for the wonderful surprise.

The Golden Rule

IT WAS a bright, cold day. Deep snow sparkled on the fields and made a crunching sound underfoot. It was perfect coasting.

Harvey, who was now seven, was watching Hiram. The hired man was trying to hitch Jennifer to the sleigh. Mrs. Firestone wanted to drive over to the Flickingers' house to take them some cream and eggs.

"Get in there!" Hiram yelled. He could not make her step between the shafts of the sleigh. She just stood there and refused to move.

"Back up!" he shouted, and then he hit her hard on the nose.

"Don't hit Jennifer!" Harvey cried. He could not bear to see any animal hurt. "You know Father wouldn't like that!"

"Mind your own business, young man. You don't need to tell me what to do around here," Hiram said. "Back up!" he cried again, but the horse stood still. This time Hiram kicked her.

Harvey could not stand by and watch the hired man hurt his father's favorite horse. "Give me the reins," he said. "I can get her in."

Hiram laughed. "A little nobody like you couldn't get that horse to move," he said. "Here." He tossed Harvey the reins. "Go ahead and try it."

Harvey was just able to reach high enough to grab the horse's chin strap. He talked gently to her. "It's all right, Jennifer," he said. "I'm your friend. I won't hit you. Just take a few steps backward, that's all."

As he talked he pushed steadily to show the

horse what he wanted her to do. Then she moved slowly in between the shafts.

"Well, I never!" Hiram exclaimed. "I don't know why she wouldn't move for me."

"Because she's afraid of you," Harvey said. "How would you like to be hit?"

Hiram did not answer. He led the horse toward the farmhouse where Mrs. Firestone was waiting for him.

Harvey was expecting George Cole to come over with his sled. They planned to go coasting on the hill above Bull Creek.

While waiting for his friend, Harvey looked for something to do. He decided to sweep the barn floor. It was covered with hay that had fallen from the hayloft. Hiram was supposed to keep the barn clean, but he was lazy.

First Harvey cleaned the floor. Then he moved some bags of oats that Hiram had left by the door. He found his father's new wrench

under one of the bags and put it in the tool box where it belonged.

"Come on, Harvey!" George Cole was standing outside. He was wearing a bright red stocking hat and red mittens.

"Be right with you," Harvey called. He ran to the house, got his sled and joined his friend. They went off across the pasture but did not see that King was following them.

The snow on the hill had been packed down by the girls and boys who had been coasting there the day before. Today the boys were alone.

"Race you to the bottom," George called as he gave his sled a push and jumped on it.

Harvey was about to shove his sled and fall on it, too, when something blocked his way. It was King. He stood in front of the sled and wagged his tail.

"Move over," Harvey said. "Get out of the

40

way, please." King, thinking Harvey wanted to play, jumped up and down like a puppy. Harvey pushed off, but King kept getting in his way. Harvey had to stop the sled several times. At last he reached the bottom of the hill.

"I beat," George said.

"King keeps getting in my way," Harvey complained. "I can't race with him around."

They pulled their sleds back to the top of the hill.

"I have an idea," George told Harvey. He took off his large red stocking hat.

"The sun is warm now. I don't need the hat. Pull it over King's head and while he's trying to take it off, we can race down the hill."

Harvey laughed. "Good idea," he said. "It won't hurt him, and anyway we didn't ask him to come with us."

The plan worked well. The boys reached the foot of the hill before King could push the hat off his head. After they did this three times the dog ran away and went home.

That noon as soon as the family sat down at the dinner table, Harvey knew something was wrong. His father hardly spoke and when he did, it seemed as if he were angry.

As Mrs. Firestone brought in a big apple pie, Mr. Firestone turned to Hiram.

"Have you remembered where you put that new wrench?" he asked. "It wasn't in the tool box this morning. We've got to tighten the bolts on the big door. It might work loose, fall, and hurt someone."

Hiram moved uneasily in his chair. "I think I left it under a bag of oats," he said.

"That's no place to leave a new tool!" Mr. Firestone declared. "Tools belong in the tool box. How many times do I have to tell you that, Hiram?"

"But I know where I left it," Hiram insisted.

42

"It isn't my fault if it wasn't there when I went for it."

Harvey knew that he must not keep quiet any longer. "I found it when I was cleaning the barn this morning and put it in the tool box," he said.

Hiram glared at the boy. "So that's what happened! If you'd stay out of the barn I'd know where things are."

"And if you'd keep the barn neat and clean as you are supposed to," Mr. Firestone added, "Harvey wouldn't find tools that belong in the tool box."

He wiped his mouth, excused himself, and left the table. As he put on his coat he said, "I'm going to fix the door now. Come on, Hiram, I'll need you."

Harvey helped his mother clear the dishes off the table. She washed the dishes and he dried them. He was so quiet that she could tell something was troubling him. When they had finished, she took off her apron and asked him to come to the sitting room.

"What's wrong, Harvey?" she asked as they sat on the sofa. "Do you have a stomachache?"

He shook his head. "I'm all right."

"No, you're not," Mrs. Firestone insisted.

"I'd rather not say." Harvey looked away from his mother. "You once told me that you didn't like tattletales."

"I don't," Mrs. Firestone admitted. "But sometimes we have to say what's on our minds. Sometimes it's best that way."

Harvey sighed. "I don't think Hiram would like me to tell," he said.

Mrs. Firestone was silent for a moment. Then she asked, "Did he do something your father would not like?"

"Yes, Mother."

"Then I think you should tell me," she said.

"I'll decide whether or not your father should know it, too."

"It's—it's just that Hiram is not nice to the animals," Harvey said.

"What do you mean?" asked his mother.

"This morning he hit Jennifer. Yesterday he hit one of the cows, and once he kicked King."

Mrs. Firestone stood up. "Hiram is a bully!" she said. "It's not wrong to tattle on a man like that. I have to tell your father about this. You know how much he loves animals."

Two days later when the family came to dinner Hiram was not at the table.

"Where's Hiram?" Harvey asked.

"I'll tell you as soon as we ask grace," Mr. Firestone said. After the blessing he stood up to carve the lamb.

"You said you'd tell us about Hiram," Harvey reminded his father.

"That's right." Mr. Firestone nodded his head

in agreement. "Well, I'm afraid Hiram Jones wasn't the kind of man who should work on a farm with animals," he said. "Fortunately, I was able to find him a good job in Columbiana at the new buggy factory. I think he'll be happier there and he'll make more money."

"The animals will be happier, too," said Harvey.

"I hope he never works on a farm again," Mrs. Firestone said. "There should be a law to protect animals against such bullies!"

"Who will take his place?" Elmer asked.

"Do you remember Pete Bunker who used to work for the Coles?" asked Mr. Firestone. "Pete likes animals and you will like him, too."

"He's the man who saved King when he fell through the ice, isn't he?" Elmer asked.

"That's right," Mr. Firestone said.

Right away Harvey knew that he was going to like the new hired man.

46

Teacher's Pet

"HARVEY! Harvey! Time to get up. You go to school today!" Mrs. Firestone called through the door to his bedroom.

"I'm up, Mother, almost ready." He had been awake for a long time wondering what school would be like. It was September and Harvey was almost eight. At that time children started school at an older age than they do now.

"It isn't every boy who can go to a brand-new school," Mr. Firestone observed at breakfast. "That Pleasant Valley School is a fine building. You should have seen the shack they called a school when I was young."

Harvey nodded and wished that he could seem more interested. As the time drew closer to leaving for school he dreaded it more. He feared that he might not do well in class. Worse still, George had told him that Paul Hanson, an older boy, was a bully who picked fights. There would also be homework that would be no fun. At least Elmer never liked it.

"I'm sure you will be a good student just as Elmer is," Mrs. Firestone said. She left the table and returned with a package. "Here's a little 'first day of school' present," she added. "Don't lose it. Father and I hope it brings you good marks."

Harvey had no idea what it was. His fingers slipped as he tried to pull the string. At last he opened the box. Inside was a real slate with a frame of pine wood. Twisted colored yarn decorated the frame and a slate pencil was tied to it with a piece of heavy string.

48

"Jumping bullfrogs!" Harvey exclaimed. "Oh, thank you, thank you very much." He slid off his chair and kissed his mother.

"That sure beats the old soapstone and piece of stone I'm using," Elmer said. "I'd like a slate, too, Mother."

His mother smiled. "You older pupils don't start school until November," she reminded him. "Maybe by that time I'll find another."

Harvey finished his breakfast.

"I'd better go," he said. "I don't want to be late the first day."

He kissed his folks good-bye and walked down the road. Mrs. Firestone stood on the porch and waved. Suddenly King came bounding out of the house and ran after Harvey.

"King, come back!" Mrs. Firestone called, but neither King nor Harvey heard her.

As he walked toward school Harvey's stomach began to feel jumpy. He was not exactly afraid, but he was not himself either. When he reached the Flickingers' house he decided to stop for a moment. Maybe he would feel better if he talked with his grandparents and Aunt Nannie for a bit, he thought.

His grandmother, a tall woman who stood very straight, greeted him with a big hug. First she wanted to see how the slate worked. Then she insisted that Harvey take one of the fresh doughnuts she had just fried.

"That will make you feel much better," she said. "You know everybody is jumpy the first day he goes to school. The feeling won't last long, though."

Harvey was glad to hear that. He thought he was the only one who was afraid.

Aunt Nannie, a pretty young woman with curly hair, came into the kitchen. She was Mrs. Firestone's sister.

"Harvey," she said, "I'm going to walk up to

the school with you and introduce you to Mr. Richards, your teacher. You wouldn't mind, would you?"

"Oh, no, Aunt Nannie," he replied, happy to have her go with him.

"Why, there's King!" Grandmother Flickinger exclaimed suddenly. "He must have followed you here." The dog walked into the kitchen and ran up to Harvey.

"I'll keep him here," Harvey's grandmother promised. "After you are in school I'll let him go home. Here, King," she called. "That's a good dog." She patted him and then shut him up in the parlor.

The school was not far beyond the Flickingers' house. It was a long building and had one room. There was a bell tower on the front. As Harvey entered he saw rows of desks and seats. Two large round iron stoves were in the middle of the room. There was a bench between the first row of desks and the teacher's desk. Each class would come up and sit here when asked to recite its lessons.

The teacher wore a black suit with long coattails. He rose from behind his desk when Aunt Nannie and Harvey entered the room.

"This is my nephew, Harvey Samuel Firestone," Aunt Nannie said as she looked down at Harvey, her hand on his shoulder.

Mr. Richards shook hands with Harvey and took him to a desk in the front row on the boys' side of the room. "You will find your books inside your desk," he said. "We start our lessons promptly at nine."

Later as Mr. Richards was teaching the alphabet to the new children, there was a loud barking at the door. Suddenly King came running down the aisle to Harvey's desk. He sat next to Harvey, thumped his tail on the floor, and licked Harvey's hand. All the pupils started to giggle and whisper. Harvey's face turned red. Why did King have to do this on the very first day of school?

"Is that your dog?" Mr. Richards asked.

"Yes, sir," Harvey said. "My grandmother said she would send him home, but I guess he came here."

"I guess he did," the teacher said. "We do not bring dogs to school. Take him outside and see that he does not come in again."

Harvey led King outside and told him to stay at the foot of the steps. At last King lay down and Harvey returned to his desk. He hoped King would stay outdoors. He would have to make certain that King did not follow him to school again tomorrow.

"School is serious business," Mr. Richards said after Harvey had come back into the room. "Those who misbehave will find that we have ways of punishing them."

He reached behind his desk and took out a
long stick.

"First we have this hickory switch which can
hurt." He replaced it and took out a dunce cap.

"Then there is this dunce cap to shame you into working harder." As he put the dunce cap back he said, "Worse yet, a bad boy will sit on the girls' side of the room."

There was no trouble the rest of that day and King did not come into the school again. As he walked home that afternoon Harvey was not sure that he liked Mr. Richards.

Every morning on the way to school Harvey stopped in at the Flickingers'. He knew that his grandmother would give him a cookie, a piece of cake, a doughnut, or whatever sweet she had on hand. Usually he walked on to school with his cousins or with new friends, one of whom was Frank Roninger.

Harvey enjoyed school and found that he liked Mr. Richards after all. The teacher made all the lessons fun.

Harvey wanted to be a good student. He had to work hard to earn good marks because he could not study easily. His grades were so good that soon some of the other children were calling him teacher's pet. They thought that Mr. Richards liked Harvey best of all the pupils.

"How's teacher's pet today?" Paul Hanson asked one morning. All the girls and boys were waiting in the school yard for the bell to ring. Paul was taller and heavier than Harvey. No one liked Paul because he was always fighting and playing mean tricks on them.

Harvey walked away from Paul, but the bigger boy followed him.

"You didn't answer my question," Paul said.

"I don't have to," Harvey answered. He wished the bell would ring so he could get away. The others crowded around.

"You want to fight?" Paul asked. He put his face up close to Harvey's.

"Not unless I have to," Harvey said, wondering how he could get away.

Paul stood firmly in Harvey's way. "Come on, teacher's pet," he said. "Bet you're too scared to fight."

Harvey remembered his mother's telling him she hoped he would never pick fights with other boys. She wanted him to fight only if he had to protect himself.

"Look here," he said as he clenched his fists. "I don't go around picking fights, but if you want trouble I'm ready for you. What's more, I'll blacken both your eyes!"

"Good for you, Harve!" Frank shouted.

No one had ever spoken to Paul like this, and he did not know what to do. Finally he smiled and stepped back. "I didn't mean any harm," he said. "I was only fooling."

"Then get out of my way," Harvey said. At this moment the bell rang and everyone ran to the door.

Paul never bothered Harvey again.

The Lost Child

"TODAY's the Village Fair!" Harvey announced as he ran downstairs to breakfast. For weeks he had looked forward to this important event. It would be his first visit to a fair and he could hardly wait.

"I want to sit next to Aunt Nannie in the carriage," he said.

"And I'm going to sit next to Grandmother Flickinger," Elmer insisted.

Mr. Firestone chuckled. "I guess we can arrange that," he said. "Nannie, Harvey, and I can sit in the front seat. Mother, Grandmother, and Elmer will sit in back. It's a good thing

58

Grandfather doesn't want to go because we have no more room."

"How about me?" Robert asked. "Where am I going to sit?"

"We've run out of space as Father said," Mrs. Firestone teased her youngest son. "I guess you will have to sit on my lap."

Harvey remembered it was not so long ago that he traveled to town sitting on his mother's knees. Now that he was eight he was too big for that, but four-year-old Robert was not.

It was a clear October morning. Usually Harvey could find plenty to do about the farm, but not today. The hours dragged and he kept running into the house to see whether it was time to get dressed. At last his mother told him he could change his clothes.

Pete Bunker, the hired man, had agreed to do everyone's chores so the family could leave before dark.

"Where's King?" Mr. Firestone asked as he stopped the buggy near the house.

"He's tied up in the barn," Harvey said. "I put him there when I went out to say good-bye to Pinto a while ago."

"Good," Mr. Firestone said. "We won't have to worry about his following us."

Elmer brought the big basket in which Mrs. Firestone had packed their picnic supper. He put it in the back of the buggy. Then the family climbed into the carriage and Jennifer galloped down the road. Harvey held on to the seat so he would not jounce off. After Aunt Nannie and Grandmother Flickinger joined them, Jennifer slowed her pace.

As they came closer to Columbiana they met other buggies headed for the fair. The sun was just setting when they turned in at the field where the fair was held. A huge crowd jammed the place.

60

s. Firestone bit her lip for a moment, then "I guess so, but remember, Harvey, you sponsible for him. Robert, you be sure to Harvey's hand all the time."

right," Mr. Firestone agreed as he ed into his pocket again. "Here's a dime bert." He looked down at his small son. ey will keep it for you and you tell him you want to buy."

vey pulled Robert away before he had a e to thank his father. The first booth they to sold homemade candy. Each of the ought a two-cent all-day sucker. Then vent on to the next booth, where all kinds etables were for sale. They passed by d the next, but at the fourth booth Robert ned, "Look at those toys, Harvey! I want ed engine!"

vey had never seen so many toys. He and looked at them for a long time. Every-

It was more beautiful than Harvey ever imagined it would be. Around the clearing there were twenty booths, each lit with lanterns or candles. Between the booths colorful Japanese lanterns swung in the light evening breeze. It looked like fairyland.

"When can we see the booths?" Harvey asked his mother.

"When do we eat?" Robert wanted to know.

"One at a time," Mrs. Firestone said, laughing. "First we'll tie up Jennifer over there by the trees. Then we'll eat our picnic supper. We can sit on the benches by that popcorn stand. After we finish eating we can see the fair. How does that strike you?"

The boys nodded in agreement.

The food was the same as they ate at home, except that it was cold. Harvey thought it was the most delicious supper he had ever eaten. They had cold fried chicken, potato salad, hard-boiled eggs, buttered rolls, pickles, and a crock of cool milk. For dessert Grandmother Flickinger brought a three-layer chocolate cake.

Frank Roninger walked by. "Hello, everybody," he called. "Having a good time?"

"We surely are," Harvey replied, "but we haven't really seen the fair yet."

"Why are you wasting your time eating when there's so much to do here?" Frank asked. He was thin because he was a poor eater.

"That's half the fun," Elmer declared as he pushed a big piece of cake into his mouth.

"It always tastes better here," Harvey added. "How about some of Grandmother's cake?" He pointed to the remains of what had been a large chocolate cake.

"Not for me, thanks," Frank said. "It might make me fat. Besides, I'm going to move along. I'll see you all later." He ran off to the nearest booth, where several people were gathered.

"I can hardly walk,"
finished his third piece o

"Then you'd better ge
Firestone advised. "Wh
they have in those booths
by the buggy when the
nine. Oh, one thing mo
his pocket and chuckled.
Elmer, and you, Harve
spend as you wish."

"A whole quarter!"
him that was a fortune.
Aren't you going to give

"He doesn't know the
Mr. Firestone said.

"I'll take him with m
it," Harvey offered.

His father scratched
"What do you think, Ca
Robert go off with Har

M
said,
are r
hold

"A
reach
for R

"Har
what

Ha
chand
came
boys
they
of ve
this a
screa
that r

Ha
Rober

thing they wanted to buy cost more money than either wanted to spend.

"Let's go on," Harvey said finally. "Christmas is coming in two months. We'll get toys then."

They continued on their way, pushing through the crowd as they visited each booth. So far they had not found anything else to buy besides the all-day suckers. When they had finished looking at the last booth where some smiling farmers' wives sold homemade jams, jellies, and bread, Harvey saw a group of men standing at one side of the field. Many of them were carrying lanterns. They were crowded about some horses that were tied to posts.

"Let's see what they're doing before we look at the booths again," Harvey said. He led his brother across the grass to the horses.

"Hi, Harve," a voice called.

"Who's that?" Harvey peered into the darkness but could not see anyone.

"Frank Roninger. Don't you know my voice?"

"Oh, of course!" Harvey was sorry that he had not recognized his friend. "What's going on here?" he asked.

"They're buying and selling horses," Frank said. "Come and watch them."

"My father could show them a thing or two," Harvey boasted. "He's a smart horse trader. I'm going to be a trader, too."

The boys watched the men as they carefully examined the horses and talked about each one. It made Harvey homesick for Pinto.

The clock struck nine.

"I have to meet the family," Harvey said. "See you in the morning at Sunday school." He turned around to take Robert's hand, but Robert was gone.

"Robert, where are you?" There was no answer. "Robert!"

Harvey's heart began to pound. Where had

66

Robert gone? He was there a moment before. "Robert! Where are you?" he called again, but there was no answer. "Frank, please help me find my brother," Harvey called into the darkness, but Frank had gone, too.

What should he do? He dreaded returning to the family without his brother, but he must get help. Frightened, he ran back to the buggy, hoping Robert would be there.

"Where's Robert?" his mother asked.

"I don't know. Isn't he here?"

"No. Where did you have him last?" Mr. Firestone asked.

"Oh, this is terrible!" Grandmother Flickinger said and started to cry.

Harvey told them about looking at the horses and meeting Frank. "While we were talking Robert must have wandered off," he said.

"All right," Mr. Firestone said in a low voice, "let's not get excited—yet. He must be around

68

somewhere. I'll take the lantern and search the area around the horses. Elmer, you start at the end of the booths and carefully look about each booth. Harvey, you start at the other end. The ladies will wait here in case Robert comes back by himself. We'll all meet here at the buggy in ten minutes."

Harvey ran off toward the first booth. He had never felt so unhappy or ashamed of himself. He almost wished his father had punished him right away, but of course the important thing was to find Robert. They *must* find Robert. How could he have been so careless?

Robert was not at the first, the second, or the third booth. Harvey ran up to the toy booth and there in front of it was Robert, playing with the toy engine.

"Robert! Oh, Robert! I'm so glad I found you!" Harvey cried.

"I want this engine," Robert said.

69

"How much is it?" Harvey asked. He was so happy to have found his brother he would have gladly given him anything.

"Thirty cents," one of the men said.

Harvey counted their money. Robert had eight cents and he had twenty-three.

"Here's thirty cents," he said as he gave the money to the clerk. "That leaves a penny, Robert. Now let's get back to the buggy."

The next morning Mr. Firestone called Harvey into the parlor and shut the door.

"You know why I sent for you?" he asked.

"Yes, Father." Harvey did not tell him that he had worried all night about what had happened and about his punishment.

"Do you realize how serious it might have been if Robert had wandered into the woods instead of back to the fair? He might have been lost and died."

Harvey bit his lip.

"I never thought of that," he admitted. "I'm very sorry. I guess I got so interested in the horses, I forgot about Robert."

"When you have a responsibility," Mr. Firestone continued, "you must make certain that you do what is expected of you. Robert was your responsibility, but you did not keep him with you. I want you to grow up to be a man who can be relied on." He studied Harvey carefully. "Have you learned a lesson from this, son?"

Harvey looked down. "Yes, Father."

"All right—and just to make certain that you don't forget it in a hurry, you may not ride Pinto for the next two weeks."

Harvey fought back the tears. Not ride his Pinto for two long weeks! How could he wait such a long time?

"Do you understand?" Mr. Firestone asked.

"Yes, Father," Harvey replied. He had indeed learned a lesson.

The Business Adventure

HARVEY wanted a horse of his own more than anything else. Elmer had Black Beauty, a fine young horse which he rode to town on Saturdays. Now that Harvey was ten, he wanted to ride with Elmer. Pinto was too small and slow to be fun. The pony was better for Robert.

"Father," Harvey said one Sunday in April as the family was riding home from church, "I want to earn money so I can buy a horse."

"That sounds like a good idea," Mr. Firestone said. "What are you planning to do?"

"I thought of raising vegetables," Harvey explained. "I could sell them to our neighbors and if I grew enough, maybe Mason's Market would buy some, too."

Mr. Firestone agreed. He always encouraged his children to try different kinds of work. "The only way you can learn whether or not something is a good idea is to try it," he would tell them.

"Remember it's going to cost you some money to get started," Mr. Firestone said after Grandmother and Grandfather Flickinger had climbed from the buggy and said good-bye to the family. "You have to buy seed. Do you have any money saved up?"

Harvey shook his head sadly. "No, Father. I spent all my money the other day for that book about horses."

"So you did," Mr. Firestone recalled. "Well, suppose I lend you two dollars."

"Jumping bullfrogs! That would be great!"

"I'm lending it to you," Mr. Firestone repeated. "You understand I expect you to repay me from your profits."

Every day after school and each Saturday Harvey worked on his garden. His father gave him a large plot of ground beyond the barn.

First the boy turned the ground over with a pitchfork, and then he raked out all the stones. The hired man brought him some well-rotted manure to spread over his earth and told him to rake it in well.

"Now you're ready for the seeds," Mr. Firestone said one Saturday morning as he examined the neat plot. "Let's go to town."

Harvey drove Jennifer all the way to Columbiana. He felt very important as he reined Jennifer in by the general store. Then he jumped down and tied her to a hitching post.

"Have you decided which vegetables you want to grow?" Mr. Firestone asked. They stood in front of the bins of seeds.

"Let's see," Harvey said as he pulled a piece of paper from his pocket on which he had made a list of the vegetables he hoped to raise. "Tomatoes, corn, potatoes, carrots, beets, squash, pumpkins, string beans, and lettuce."

"I wouldn't bother with the carrots and the beets," Mr. Firestone advised. "Most people grow them in their own gardens. They won't be worth your time."

A clerk weighed out the seed and put each kind in a little bag. Next Mr. Firestone bought seed for the family garden, including corn, beans, and other kinds of vegetables. Then he picked out a brand new hoe.

"This hoe is a present for you." He handed it to Harvey. "You can't garden properly if you let the weeds grow. Now you can have the best-looking garden in all Columbiana!"

That afternoon he showed Harvey how to lay out the rows with string. He explained how deep each kind of seed should be planted. When they had finished planting the seeds and covering them with dirt, Harvey stood back and looked at his garden.

"I'm going to be a farmer when I grow up," he declared. "What an easy way to make money! Now I just have to wait for the crops to grow, then I'll buy my horse!"

Mr. Firestone smiled. "It's not that easy, son," he said, "or I'd be that kind of a farmer, too. Why do you think I raise sheep and wheat but no other crops?"

Harvey shrugged his shoulders.

"Because sheep and wheat bring more money for less work," Mr. Firestone said. "I don't have to worry about bugs and the weather." He shook his finger at Harvey. "You'll see."

Harvey said nothing. He was certain that his father was wrong so far as *his* garden would be concerned. He would keep the weeds down, he would even carry buckets of water to keep the plants moist if necessary. Raising crops was not that difficult. He would have that horse by the end of the summer.

At first it looked as if Harvey was right. Under the gentle spring rains and warm sunshine, the seeds sprouted quickly and sent up their first shoots. Each day the green plants seemed to have grown overnight.

"You should see my garden!" Harvey told his mother one day. "I'm going to make a lot of money and get that horse."

"Harvey," Mrs. Firestone said quietly, wondering how to prepare him for possible disappointment, "I hope I'm wrong in what I'm going to say." She put her hand on his shoulder. "There is always the chance that something may happen to your garden. Remember how Mr. Cole lost all his corn and potatoes last year?"

Harvey nodded.

"The same thing can happen to anyone," Mrs. Firestone continued. "It's just that I want you to be prepared in case things don't go as you expect."

"Thank you, Mother," Harvey said. He was not worried about his little garden behind the barn. What could go wrong?

One morning two weeks later on the way to school, he stopped to look at his vegetables.

"Jumping bullfrogs!" he muttered as he stared at the string beans. "What happened?" Where there had been a row of plants, each with two new leaves, now there was only a row of short green stalks.

He felt a sinking feeling in his stomach. How did this happen? Why did some animal have to do it? All was not lost, however. There were still three rows of beans, but who knew when the rabbit or woodchuck might return again?

That night Harvey asked if he could sleep outdoors by the garden.

"Heavens, no!" his mother said. "You'd catch your death of cold on the damp ground at this time of the year."

"Once you're asleep those animals will take what they want anyway," Mr. Firestone added. "Many farmers grow more than they need so that animals will have their share."

"But I need to sell everything I grow so I can get a horse," Harvey insisted. "I'm not interested in feeding wild animals."

"That's one reason why I'm not a farmer," his father said and chuckled to himself.

The rabbits and woodchucks later helped themselves to more beans and some of the lettuce. Fortunately the corn grew well, but in July there was little rain and August was very dry. Harvey tried carrying water in a pail from the pump in the kitchen. He soon found that his garden was much too large to water that way and he gave up the idea.

"Golly, I'm never going to get that horse the way things are going," he told George Cole one day. "I've only sold a little lettuce, some tomatoes, and beans to my mother and my Grandmother. Tomorrow I'm going to town and sell my vegetables to Mason's Market."

Harvey got up early the next morning and picked all the vegetables that were ripe. He and his mother drove into Columbiana and went straight to Mason's Market.

"I have some fine fresh vegetables outside," Harvey told Mr. Mason. "Are you interested in buying them?"

Mr. Mason shook his head sadly. "Sorry, Harvey," he said. "I've got all I need. Several local farmers bring them in to me. Maybe you could sell some of your vegetables if you went to people's homes."

"Thank you," Harvey said and returned to the buggy. He had never dreamed he could not sell his vegetables to the store.

"We can stop at a few of the houses on our way home," his mother suggested when he told her what Mr. Mason said. "I'm sure some of our neighbors will buy from you."

Most people had enough vegetables for the weekend. Because of this Harvey found that he had to reduce his prices in order to sell what he had picked.

"Let's pull into the Roningers' farm, Mother," Harvey suggested.

As they drove up Mrs. Roninger came out, wiping her hands on her clean white apron.

"Do you want to buy some tomatoes and beans, Mrs. Roninger?" Harvey asked. "They're in the back of the buggy."

Mrs. Roninger looked over the vegetables for a moment. "That's just what I need," she said and she winked so that only Mrs. Firestone could see. "I'll get some money from my purse."

Harvey was happy that he could sell the rest of his vegetables.

"It was a good thing we came along," he observed as they drove on home. "She was the only customer who seemed glad to see us."

Mrs. Firestone tried not to laugh. She sat very still for a few minutes. Then she said, "Harvey, Mrs. Roninger did not need those vegetables. She only bought them to help you."

"How do you know?" Harvey was sorry to hear this. He thought Mrs. Roninger really wanted his tomatoes and beans.

"Oh, I know all right, but don't you let it bother you," his mother answered. "I bought the saddle soap and cheap perfume her son Frank was selling last week. We mothers are glad to help out one another's children."

"I don't think much of this farming business,"

Harvey remarked at the dinner table that night. "The animals, the heat, and the dry spell take half your crops. Then when you go to sell your vegetables, nobody wants to buy them. What is the use?"

"You understand now why I steered clear of farming?" Mr. Firestone asked.

"I sure do," Harvey replied. "One thing I know is that I never want to be a farmer. After I pay you back the two dollars you lent me for the seed, I'll have about seven dollars left over. I'll never get the horse."

"Lucky you don't have to live on that money," Elmer said. "You wouldn't stay alive long on seven dollars for a whole summer's work!"

"If I can't make money in a business, there's no sense bothering," Harvey said. "Next summer I'll look for something better to do. Maybe I'll make enough money then to get my horse."

84

The Trapped Cat

"Harve, come on, we're going hunting," George Cole called. He and Eddie Wilson were standing on the porch. Each carried a gun.

Harvey came to the door. "What's the matter with you fellows?" he asked. "Don't you know it's Sunday?"

George nodded. "Sure. Wasn't I in Sunday school today?"

"Doesn't Sunday mean anything in your family?" Harvey asked.

"Yes," Eddie replied. "We always have a stewed chicken with dumplings. What are you getting at, Harve?" He was taller than Harvey or George and had red hair and a mole on the end of his nose.

"Sunday's a special day," Harvey explained. "My father calls it the *Lord's Day*. We don't do any work except the necessary chores. We don't hunt, fish, or fool around."

Eddie looked at George and scratched his head. "What a sissy idea," he said. "You're worse than a girl, Harve." He picked up his gun. "Let's go, George."

"I'm no sissy," Harvey said. "Besides, Eddie, I like having Sunday this way. I'll meet you at George's house tomorrow morning if you want to go hunting then."

Harvey had received a Spencer rifle for his eleventh birthday. Mr. Firestone taught him how to shoot but forbade him to go hunting alone. "When you're fourteen," he said, "you may go out by yourself to hunt, but until then I want you to be with others."

The next morning Harvey and King went over to the Coles' home where George and Eddie were waiting for him.

"A woodchuck has been eating our corn," George said. "Let's see if we can find him."

The boys walked to the cornfield, singing "Yankee Doodle" as they went. Suddenly Eddie stopped and pointed to a nearby tree.

"Hey, look at that robin up there!" he said. "Let's see who can hit it."

He quickly cocked his gun, took aim, and fired. The bird trembled for a few seconds and fell to the ground dead.

"Good shot, Eddie!" George cried.

Harvey was so surprised and shocked that he could hardly speak. A minute before the bird was up there on the branch singing. Now, for no reason, it was dead.

"Why did you do that?" Harvey asked. "Why did you kill the bird?"

"Why not?" Eddie wanted to know. "What do you think guns are for?"

"Not to kill without a reason," Harvey said. "Suppose that bird has a nest of young ones? What will happen to them now?"

Eddie had not thought of that. "I don't know," he said.

"That's wrong," Harvey told him. "My father told me that guns should be used only to get food or to protect ourselves."

"Those are your rules," Eddie muttered. "I have my own and I'll follow them."

The boys looked for the woodchuck but did not find him. King, who was growing old, came trotting behind them. He was not interested in smelling the ground or chasing squirrels.

The weather was turning hot, and the boys soon lost interest in their hunt.

"What do you say we go down to Bull Creek and have a swim?" George suggested.

"Good idea," Harvey said. The hunting had not been much fun after all.

The boys went back past George's house and cut across the fields toward the swimming hole. Suddenly King dashed ahead of them, bounded up to a stone wall, and began to bark. The boys ran up to see what he had found.

George leaned down and searched. "Hey, there's a big brown cat in here," he said. "It's head is caught between two stones. Good thing King can't reach it!"

Eddie looked next. "Just an old cat," he said. "I'm going to shoot it."

Harvey's fingers tightened about his gun. "No, you're not!" he said. "Put down that gun, Eddie Wilson." He moved over toward the cat and stood in front of the wall.

Eddie shook his head. "You're nothing but a sissy, Harve. I'm not going hunting with you again." He lowered his gun and started to walk

away. "George," he called over his shoulder, "let him have his old cat if he wants. We'll go swimming."

"Come on, Harve," George said. "Leave the cat. It got there, it can get out again. Cats can take care of themselves."

"How would you like to be stuck in a stone wall?" Harvey said. "If another animal comes along the cat couldn't defend itself."

George did not hear what Harvey said. He was running to catch up with Eddie.

Harvey leaned down and tried to reach in to free the cat. Every time he almost touched her she hissed and bared her teeth.

"I'm not going to hurt you, Kitty," he said, but the cat paid no attention.

Harvey studied the wall and saw that if he took off the stones he could free the cat. With difficulty he moved several of them, but those near the bottom were too heavy.

He sat down for a moment. He was hot and tired. A swim would feel good. George and Eddie were probably splashing about in the water by now. Why shouldn't he join them?

As he walked away King started to bark again. Harvey knew that somehow he had to set the animal free. He could not go swimming. Instead he must find help, but where? George and Eddie wouldn't do anything. There was no place to go except home.

"Come on, King!" he called as he started, but King would not move. The more Harvey called the louder King barked. Harvey knew that as long as King stayed there the cat would be safe from other animals.

He hurried home, found his mother, and told her about the cat.

"I wonder if it's Mrs. Dowling's cat," she said. "She's the only person here who has one."

"I don't know," Harvey said. "Do you suppose Father would mind if I asked Pete to come back with me and help free the cat?"

"Of course not!" Mrs. Firestone said. "Your father doesn't like to see any animal suffer. Just be careful. Take a burlap bag or something to keep from being scratched."

Harvey found the hired man cutting hay. He explained why he needed his help. "And Mother says it is all right for you to come with me," he added.

"Glad to help any time," Pete said. "You lead the way."

It was easy to find where the cat was trapped because King was still standing by the wall barking. Pete got down on his hands and knees and studied the cat carefully.

"I don't see how she ever got in there," he said. "Hand me that burlap and I'll see if I can lift her over that stone that sticks up."

The cat hissed as Pete, his right hand

wrapped in burlap, tugged at her. "It's no use," he said. "I'm afraid I'll hurt her."

"Then we'll have to take the stones off," Harvey said. Together they were able to roll the rocks back. At last there was left only the big stone that held the cat.

"I'll pry it with this stick," Pete said. He moved the rock slowly until there was just enough room for the cat to get out. She jumped up and streaked off across the field with King chasing after her.

"Jumping bullfrogs!" Harvey said. "I forgot all about King!"

"Don't worry," Pete said. "That cat's so scared she could outrun the swiftest deer. Now we have to put the wall back. Mr. Cole wouldn't like us to leave it this way."

When they returned home Harvey saw their neighbor, Mrs. Dowling, standing on the porch talking with his mother.

"Harvey, was that my brown cat, Fluffy?" Mrs. Dowling called.

"It was a brown cat," Harvey answered.

"Where is she? Where is she?" Mrs. Dowling came running toward him.

Harvey laughed. "By now she's probably at home. I never saw a cat run so fast!"

"Harvey!" Mrs. Dowling shook her finger at him. "How dare you chase my poor cat?"

"I didn't chase her," Harvey said. "It was King who chased her after Pete and I moved the stones that held her in the wall."

Mrs. Dowling covered her mouth with her hand. "So that's what happened!" she said. "Why—I—I don't know how to thank you. If you hadn't found my Fluffy she would still be there and nobody would know where to look for her."

Harvey patted King. "Don't thank me," he said. "It was King, not I, who found your cat."

The Drummers

"Why will I see a lot of drummers down by the station?" Harvey asked his father. "Is there going to be a band concert?"

Mr. Firestone shook his head and snapped the reins to make the horse trot faster.

"The answer to your first question is that today is Friday and this is the day the drummers go home," he said. "Your second question calls for a no." He smiled at his son and added, "They aren't drummers with drums. Drummer is a word that means someone whose business is selling. He goes out and drums up business. That is how he got his name."

96

"Oh, I see," Harvey said, smiling. "Someday I'd like to be a drummer and go places. I want to travel and see the world."

"There's plenty of time for that," Mr. Firestone said. "Look there! Aren't those apple blossoms pretty?" He pointed to a large tree that looked as if it were covered with snow instead of blossoms. "I think spring is my favorite season," he said quietly.

But Harvey was not listening. He was thinking of Will Green who had just quit school and had gone to Detroit to spend the summer on his uncle's farm. Harvey was having trouble with his history lessons. In a way he wished he could have gone with Will.

They came to the railroad track at the foot of Main Street. As soon as they crossed it Mr. Firestone guided the buggy past the big hotel and drew up at the station. He jumped to the ground and hitched Nelly to a post. A number of men were standing on the platform. Each had a suitcase and one or more boxes that held samples and the goods they sold as they traveled to the nearby towns.

"Are they the drummers?" Harvey asked.

Mr. Firestone nodded. "Yes, but don't call them that to their faces. It would not be respectful." Then he told Harvey that he had to talk with the station agent about a shipment of grain he had ordered.

"May I wait here on the platform?" Harvey asked, excited at the chance of possibly seeing a train.

"Yes, but stand back if a train comes," Mr. Firestone warned. He went into the station and Harvey walked around the gray building to the narrow wooden platform where he pushed his way past the men and stood as close to the shiny steel rails as he could get.

He looked up and down the track, but no train

was in sight. He hoped that one would come before his father finished his business with the station agent.

Harvey turned around and looked at the men. Most of them wore black derby hats and had large bushy moustaches. His father had told him that they always came to Columbiana on the Monday train and left Friday.

A tall, thin man walked up to him.

"How old are you, son?" he asked.

"Twelve, sir," the boy replied.

"You remind me of Ned, my lad at home," the drummer said. "He's lazy, though," he added. "Are you lazy?"

"No, sir—at least I don't think I am."

"That's good." The drummer shook his head slowly. "I would like to teach Ned my business, but he isn't interested." He stared at Harvey. "I could use someone like you to help me. You could carry my samples and show them to the customers." Then he laughed. "We'd make quite a pair, wouldn't we!"

"You—you mean you could use me?" Harvey stammered, not certain that he had heard the man correctly. Maybe he could ride the train and travel after all!

"Yes, that's what I said."

"What do you sell?" Harvey asked.

"Supplies for horses. Harnesses, bridles, bits, spurs, whips, crops, and things like that. What's your name, son? Mine's Thomas, Howard Thomas." He held out his hand.

"Harvey Firestone," the boy replied as they shook hands. "I like horses. Someday I'm going to buy a horse of my own."

"That's fine. I hope——"

A sharp whistle interrupted Mr. Thomas and Harvey never learned what he was hoping. The rails began to hum as the train came into sight. Harvey stepped back and watched the big en-

100

gine approach the station, its brakes screeching and sparks shooting from the wheels. He wished he could climb aboard with the drummers.

" 'Bye," Mr. Thomas called as he picked up his bag and boxes and ran up the steps of the passenger coach.

"Good-bye, Mr. Thomas," Harvey called to his new friend, but he did not think he heard him above the noise of the other men shouting to one another.

Suddenly the train lurched forward as the engine chugged and the four cars moved slowly from the station. Harvey watched the train disappear down the track and around the curve in the distance. He was alone on the platform. It was quiet now except for the clicking of the telegraph machine inside the station.

A moment later Mr. Firestone appeared. They climbed into the buggy and headed for home. Somehow Harvey did not want to tell his father about Mr. Thomas. He hoped to keep it a secret but wondered when he would see the friendly drummer again.

The following Monday, as soon as school was dismissed, Harvey hurried home ahead of all the others. He was ashamed of himself because he had failed the history test. He knew that the teacher was surprised and disappointed.

As he crossed the bridge over Bull Creek, he felt like throwing his books into the water and forgetting all about school. Wasn't he old enough to leave school and work somewhere on a farm or in a store? Will Green had quit. Why shouldn't he too stop studying so he could earn money and have fun?

He thought of Mr. Thomas, the drummer, and what he had said Friday at the station. Harvey could still hear his deep voice: "I could use someone like you to help me."

That was it! Maybe he could not do history,

but Mr. Thomas thought he was smart. Why not ask the drummer if he could have that job? Harvey grinned as he pictured himself traveling everywhere on the trains and earning enough money to buy his own horse.

By the time he reached home he had decided to go straight to town. It was Monday, so Mr. Thomas should be at the hotel.

Harvey found Pete, the hired man, cleaning out the chicken coop.

"Everyone's gone to Columbiana to buy seeds," Pete said. "I expect them back soon."

Harvey did not want to see his mother or father before he talked with Mr. Thomas. Instead of taking the road to town, he decided to use a shortcut that led through the fields and along the railroad track. Without telling Pete where he was going, Harvey went through the yard, jumped over the fence, and ran across the pasture and on through the green meadows beyond.

When he reached the track he was out of breath, but he hurried along just the same.

As soon as he reached the Main Street crossing, Harvey left the track and walked up to the hotel. He had never been in a hotel before and was not sure what he should do or say. He opened the front door slowly and saw the large lobby which was filled with chairs. Then he went inside and looked about him to see if he could find Mr. Thomas.

"What do you want here, boy?" a man called in an annoyed tone of voice from behind a long counter at one end of the lobby.

"I want to talk with Mr. Thomas," Harvey said, his voice trembling.

The man looked in a large book. "He isn't here. He may be coming on the afternoon train." He turned and looked out the window. "There it is now!"

Harvey heard the whistle and without stop-

104

ping to thank the man for his help, ran from the lobby and down the street to the station. The train was hissing to a stop and a number of drummers were getting off, but Harvey did not

see Mr. Thomas. Soon he was alone on the platform. The train had puffed away and all the drummers had walked up to the hotel.

He was so disappointed that he almost cried. What could he do now? Where was Mr. Thomas? Why had he not returned to Columbiana? Now Harvey would have to face his parents and his teacher after all. He thought about all these things as he walked back to the farm.

It was almost dark when he left the road and came up the winding driveway to the house.

"There he is! Harvey's home!" his mother called from the back door. She ran down the steps and hurried toward him.

"Where have you been? What happened to you?" she asked. "We've been so worried! Your father is just hitching up the buggy again. He was going to look for you."

She shook her head. "Why didn't you tell Pete where you were going?"

"I'm sorry, Mother," he said. "I didn't want you to know I had gone to town."

Mrs. Firestone put her hands on her hips. "I hope you are ready to explain your actions to your father," she said.

Harvey wished he did not have to talk with his father. He knew that Mr. Firestone was always fair and did not whip his sons as some fathers did, although he punished them in other ways. The truth was that Harvey was so fond of his father that he felt bad whenever he made Mr. Firestone unhappy.

Harvey followed his mother to the house. Just then Mr. Firestone came from the barn.

"Let's go in, Harvey," he said. His voice did not sound angry. "I want you to tell me what you have been doing."

They went into the front parlor, which was used only for entertaining company and for scolding the children when they were naughty.

"Now, then," Mr. Firestone said when they were seated. "Tell me where you went."

Harvey squirmed in his chair and looked down at the floor. He told how he had failed the history test and why he had gone to the hotel hoping to meet Mr. Thomas.

"I wasn't running away, Father," he said, as he took a deep breath. "I thought that if Mr. Thomas would just give me the job I'd come home and get my clothes and say good-bye to you and Mother before I left."

He dreaded hearing what his father was going to say. If only he were on a train now instead of sitting here in the parlor!

"I'm disappointed in you, Harvey, for two reasons," Mr. Firestone said firmly. "First, you broke a family rule and left the farm without telling anyone where you were going. Second, you were ready to accept a failure without trying to overcome it."

108

Harvey knew that his father was right. He had not even talked to the teacher or asked for help so that he could get better grades.

"As for leaving school and going to work," Mr. Firestone continued, "it's true that some boys your age have to earn money to help their families and some are such poor students that they have to leave school. But you are a bright boy and always get good marks—that is, except perhaps in history."

"What good is history if you want to be a drummer?" Harvey wanted to know.

Mr. Firestone thought for a moment. "I'm not sure," he admitted, "but you will be a better and a smarter drummer if you do finish school. You have a lifetime ahead of you to earn money. Take advantage of school while you can. Every boy does not have the chance to go to school."

Harvey nodded his head in agreement. What his father said made sense.

"Now, as for the punishment—" and Harvey's heart skipped a beat—"I'm going to forget it this time if you are willing to master that history. Your mother can help you and I shall expect to see a report card next month with a good passing grade. Do you think you can do that?"

"Yes, Father, yes!" Harvey exclaimed, grateful for his father's understanding and patience.

How fortunate he had not found Mr. Thomas at the hotel!

Breaking the Colt

HARVEY stood by the fence at the upper pasture looking at his father's new horse. She was brown except for a white marking between her eyes, and not fully grown. The young horse was graceful as she walked and fast when she galloped playfully about the field.

During July Harvey had spent most of his time working on the farm with his father. Robert was still too young to be of much help and Elmer had taken a job in town. At thirteen Harvey was slim and wiry.

With four hundred sheep Harvey and his father always found something to do. The sheep needed no care because they stayed out in the pasture, but sick animals had to be looked after, and fences had to be mended.

Every day one or two of the sheep hurt their legs, bruised their bodies, or needed attention of some kind. Mr. Firestone would put these animals in the wagon and take them to the barn to work on them. From time to time Harvey would find a new-born lamb standing close to its mother.

After lunch, if the weather was good, Harvey and his father painted the barns and outbuildings. Mr. Firestone believed in keeping the farm neat and in good repair.

Now it was late in the afternoon and Harvey was taking a rest. He never let a chance go by to watch the horses and colts.

"Harvey!"

The boy jumped and turned around. "Oh, it's you, Father. I guess I was dreaming."

"Of horses?" Mr. Firestone chuckled. "Which one in particular?"

"That brown one." Harvey pointed to the one he liked best.

"I was thinking," Mr. Firestone said and then he paused.

"Yes?" Harvey asked, anxious to know what his father had in mind.

"I was thinking that if you work as well the rest of the summer as you have during July I—I just might give you a horse and——"

"Oh, Father!" Harvey interrupted. "Do you really mean it? Can I have that brown one? I have a name for her now."

Mr. Firestone laughed. "Just a minute, I haven't finished."

"Excuse me," Harvey said.

"You may keep the horse if you learn to ride her. It's one thing to ride a pony like Pinto and another to ride a horse like——" He paused and chuckled. "What did you say her name is, Harvey?"

"Kitty!" Harvey almost shouted. "I think that's a nice name for a horse." He was so excited that he did not realize how loudly he was speaking. "When may I ride her, when may I have her and feed her?"

"Let's say she is yours now, provided you do a good job the rest of the summer and learn to ride her."

"I'll get on her right away!" Harvey said, and he started to climb over the fence. He ran toward Kitty, but when she saw him coming she reared up and galloped away from him. He chased his horse for some time but did not manage to catch her.

Mr. Firestone was watching from the fence. "Harvey, come here," he called.

Harvey ran up to him, panting.

"Go and get a pail of oats," his father said.

"Next time don't run toward the horse that way. You frighten her. Walk slowly toward her and talk to her gently. Hold out the oats so she can smell them. She may not come the first time, but sometime she'll want those oats. If you don't frighten her she will come."

Harvey ran down to the barn, filled a pail with oats, and brought it back to the field. Then he slowly climbed over the fence and walked toward his horse. She watched him as he came closer. Just as he thought she was going to taste the oats, Kitty shied to one side and galloped away, across the pasture.

"That's good enough for today," his father called. "Leave her alone now and try to feed her again tomorrow afternoon."

At dinner Harvey told his mother about his new horse.

"Don't you think it's dangerous for Harvey to ride an animal like that?" she asked.

"It's a gentle horse," Mr. Firestone assured her. "She was broken in when I bought her and I've ridden her several times. Now I want Harvey to get the horse used to him." He looked at his son. "Tell Mother the name you've picked out for her."

"Kitty," Harvey said.

"I like that!" Mrs. Firestone clapped her hands with delight. "I suppose it really is a cat's name, but there's no reason why a horse can't have it if you want it that way."

Harvey was glad his mother liked the name. What she thought was important to him.

The next afternoon Kitty shied away from Harvey each time he came toward her with the pail of oats. On the following day he was successful, however. As soon as he appeared at the pasture the horse trotted over to him and began to eat from the pail.

"Don't try to mount her today," Mr. Fire-

116

stone called from the fence where he was watching. "Wait until tomorrow."

It rained so hard the next day that Harvey and his father could not work outdoors. Harvey was afraid Kitty might forget him. The next afternoon he could hardly wait to finish painting. He filled the pail quickly with oats, grabbed a bridle, and hurried to the pasture. The horse came straight to him and started to eat from the pail.

"Now put the bridle on your horse and get up on her," Mr. Firestone called. "She's ready to be ridden now."

Harvey fastened the bridle. Next he placed one hand on Kitty's neck and the other on her back and jumped and pushed himself up. Kitty was surprised. She turned her head to see what had happened, then started to run.

"Hang on, Harvey!" Mr. Firestone shouted. "Let her know you're the master."

Kitty ran halfway down the field, circled around, and galloped back. Then she turned and ran across the pasture again. The wind whistled past Harvey as he leaned forward over her neck, bouncing up and down as she ran.

"It's all right, Kitty," he half whispered in her ear. "It's Harvey, your friend."

There was no doubt in Harvey's mind that this was *his* horse. He knew that they would be friends. He pulled back on the reins and Kitty stopped in front of his father.

"Good boy!" Mr. Firestone said. "Now get down. Tomorrow we'll hitch her to the light wagon and let her get used to that."

Every afternoon after he finished his chores Harvey rode Kitty or hitched her to the wagon. He drove her up and down the road in front of the house. He hoped that he would be able to show his father that he could ride and drive well. He had to!

Harvey wanted a saddle for Kitty.

"Men don't ride sitting on blankets," he told his father one day.

"That's true," Mr. Firestone admitted. "I'll see what I can do about it."

The next afternoon he and Harvey hitched two of the horses to the big wagon to take a load of grain to town. After they had unloaded the bags at the mill Mr. Firestone drove up to the general store.

"Let's go in and pick out a new saddle, son," he said.

"Do you really mean it?" Harvey asked, surprised that his father would buy him one so soon. They entered the store and Harvey chose a saddle that resembled Elmer's.

When they returned home and Harvey showed the saddle to his mother she frowned.

"Do you think he'll be safe on that, Benjamin? It looks very large for him."

"Harvey's a good horseman," Mr. Firestone assured his wife. "He'll become used to it in no time. Don't worry about him."

One Saturday late in August the whole family, except Harvey, went to town to shop. They took Pete with them because he needed a haircut. Harvey was alone outside the barn, brushing Kitty, when Frank Roninger rode up.

"Harve!" he shouted. "Some of your sheep got out of the pasture. They're starting down the road toward Columbiana. You'd better get them back in before they get away."

"What happened?" Harvey asked. His heart was pounding. What would his father say when he learned the sheep were gone?

"I don't know. The fence is broken and they got out somehow," Frank said. "You'd better tell your father."

"He's gone to town. There's no one here except Kitty and me."

"I'll help you," Frank offered.

"Good." Harvey jumped up on Kitty and the two boys raced across the meadows toward the large field where the sheep were grazing. When they came to the place where the fence had broken, they found all of the sheep were trying to get through to the road.

"You turn them back into the field and scatter them," Harvey said. "I'll go down the road and drive the rest back."

Somehow Harvey managed to guide Kitty through the crowd of woolly animals. Kitty made her way carefully along the side of the road. When she passed the first sheep, Harvey turned her around so that she blocked the way.

"Go on—go back!" he shouted. The sheep stopped and looked at him through blinking eyes. Kitty stepped toward them and the leading sheep turned to get away from her.

Two of the leading sheep moved to the side

122

of the road and then ran back past the rest of the flock. Seeing them go, the rest of the animals turned and followed them, encouraged by Harvey's shouts.

Fortunately the leaders went through the fence back into the pasture. In a few minutes Harvey had all of the sheep safely inside. He slid off Kitty and found some branches to block the hole in the fence.

Then he noticed his father standing on the other side of the fence.

"I'm very proud of you, Harvey," he was saying. Then he chuckled.

"You—you mean you saw what happened?" Harvey asked, surprised.

"We were driving home and watched the whole thing," his father explained. "You were so busy you didn't even know we were in the road there ahead of you. But I can see that you know how to ride. You and Kitty are a good team. There's no question about it, she's your horse and you have earned her."

His words made Harvey so happy that he hardly knew what to say.

"Thank you, Father, thank you," he murmured as he stroked Kitty's side. He looked up at his horse and went on, "I'm very proud of you, too, Kitty. I guess we are a good team."

Learning
to Trade

"How would you like to go to the fair in Salem today?" Mr. Firestone asked Harvey. "The Stock Growers' Association is meeting on the fairgrounds there."

"That would be great," Harvey replied. "Are you planning to buy or sell any horses?"

"Now that you have Kitty we don't need three riding horses," Mr. Firestone said. "I think I'll sell Flash and trade Robin for another work horse. We could use another one."

"May Kitty pull the small buggy?" Harvey asked eagerly.

"Fine," his father agreed. "Why don't you

hitch her up and get the other horses ready while I go check the sheep."

Harvey hurried out to the barn. First he brushed Kitty until her coat shone. He liked to take her places and it made him proud when people admired her.

After he had hitched Kitty to the buggy he put bridles on Flash and Robin. Then he led them out and tied them to the back of the carriage. Just then Mr. Firestone came from the house carrying a wicker basket.

"All set?" he called. "Mother put up a lunch for us. I guess we won't go hungry today."

"Not with Mother's food," Harvey agreed. "I hope she put in some of that leftover chicken from last night."

As they rode toward the fair Mr. Firestone told Harvey much about buying and selling horses and how to judge them. "You can tell a horse's age by his teeth," he explained. "The

126

teeth stick out somewhat in a young horse, and an older horse shows his age when his teeth are worn down."

He told Harvey some of the secrets about listening to a horse breathe. "If the breathing sounds dry the animal probably has dust in his lungs. After a horse has exercised, if he coughs or you see the skin over his stomach ripple, beware!"

Harvey remembered every word. He had decided that when he grew up he was going to be a horse trader, not a farmer.

Within an hour they reached the fairgrounds. A band was playing lively marching music. There were many small tents. In some farmers showed their livestock. In others women exhibited cakes, pies, jams, and jellies. In one large tent several companies sold things that farmers used every day.

Harvey was interested in only one thing—the

horse trading. He and his father drove on through the fair and at the back he saw a sign: "Stock Growers' Association."

"Pull up over there away from the crowd," Mr. Firestone advised. "We'll leave the horses and see what is what."

They tied Kitty to a fence post and left the two horses standing behind the buggy. Then they walked slowly toward the group of traders.

"I follow two rules when I trade," Mr. Firestone said in a low voice. "First, I never appear anxious to buy or sell. Second, I am honest in every way." He explained that because there were so many dishonest traders, one had to be on guard. "I always tell the truth—just as you do," Mr. Firestone said, "but I am not always sure that the other fellow is telling me the truth."

They stopped to listen to two men bargaining over a horse.

"I told you that old nag isn't worth forty dollars," said a man who was buying horses. "Twenty-five is the most I'll give you."

"You don't know a good horse when you see one," the seller said. "But I'll let you have her for thirty-five."

The buyer looked at the horse again.

"Thirty dollars," he said.

"Sold!" said the seller.

Mr. Firestone looked at Harvey and chuckled. "It usually ends quickly, just like that," he said. "What takes the most time is looking over a horse and talking about its good points and its bad points."

A large man, wearing a dirty hat came toward them. "Hey, Firestone," he called. "What have you got to sell?"

Mr. Firestone tilted his head to one side. "I'm not sure I'm going to sell anything."

"Come on, I saw you drive in with two nags

behind the buggy. You didn't bring them to the fair to hear the band play."

"Maybe not," Mr. Firestone admitted, "but I haven't offered them for sale either."

The man insisted on seeing the horses and while he examined them carefully Mr. Firestone whispered to Harvey, "Never reach in on a deal. Let it come to you. That's Jack Dunbar. He's one of the traders you can't always trust. I don't mind selling to him, but I rarely buy any of his horses."

"What do you want for the black one?" the trader asked.

"Fifty dollars," Mr. Firestone said.

"That's crazy!" Mr. Dunbar protested. "I won't even try her out at that price. If she's as good as I think she is, I'll give you thirty dollars for her."

"Try her out," Mr. Firestone said. "Then you'll see why I'm asking fifty."

130

While Mr. Dunbar rode Flash around the fairgrounds, Mr. Firestone told Harvey that he always set his price about ten dollars higher than he expected to get. "That way I can come down a bit and not lose money," he said.

"The horse is worth thirty-five," Mr. Dunbar said when he returned.

"All right," Mr. Firestone said, "you like her so much I'll let you have her for forty."

Mr. Dunbar shook his head slowly. "You are a hard bargainer, but it's a deal."

"Fine," Mr. Firestone said. "Now my son here, Harvey, wants to trade this other horse for a work horse."

Harvey was surprised. He did not expect his father to let him do any trading.

Mr. Dunbar smiled and rubbed his hands together. "Breaking him in, eh? Well, it so happens I have a very nice work horse. Come on over, sonny, and I'll let you see him."

They walked over to a grove of trees nearby
where several horses were tied. Mr. Dunbar
brought out a large heavy horse. Harvey's eyes
darted here and there over the animal, looking

for signs of something wrong. Suddenly he noticed that the horse's right front leg had a slight limp.

"The horse has a limp," he said to his father. "Let's look at that leg." He examined the leg carefully and found a bad sore on the knee. "I don't think we want to take that horse," he said to Mr. Dunbar.

The trader took off his hat and scratched his bald head. "Your son is just like you, Firestone," he said. Then he smiled and put his hat on. "Now I'll show you a real good horse."

He led the lame horse away and returned a few minutes later with another.

"Her name is Feather," he said, grinning. "Look her over."

Mr. Firestone stood silently with his arms folded as Harvey examined the horse's teeth, listened to her breathing, and felt her body. Then he led Feather in a wide circle and brought her back to his father. He listened again to her breathing and watched her stomach.

"She looks all right to me, Father," he said. "What do you think?"

Mr. Firestone examined the horse briefly and stepped back. "I agree," he said. "Now go ahead and trade it for Robin."

"Are you willing to let us have this horse in exchange for ours?" Harvey asked.

Mr. Dunbar nodded. "Sure, but I want twenty dollars in the bargain."

Harvey gulped. He had never expected the trader to demand money, too. His father had not warned him about this. What should he do? Then he remembered what his father had said: "Never reach in on a deal."

Harvey waited a moment, then said, "I guess I'm not interested in your horse, Mr. Dunbar. There must be other traders who would like Robin. What do you think, Father?"

Mr. Firestone smiled. "Whatever you say, son. Robin's a good riding horse. We can sell her, buy a work horse, and make a little money on the deal, too."

While they were talking Mr. Dunbar was looking Robin over. He shook his head.

"Can't beat the two of you," he said. "All right, even trade, but I'll never do business with either of you again!"

Later Harvey and his father ate their lunch by the bandstand.

"That was good work, son," Mr. Firestone said. "I'm going to let you do much of the trading for the farm. I'll teach you about the chickens and sheep, too. Who knows, someday maybe you'll become a famous trader."

Harvey was happy. He wanted to please his father, but most of all he wanted to become a horse trader when he finished school.

An Important Decision

HARVEY was walking home with his teacher Mr. Rothwell. He often did this, for he liked to talk with the teacher. There was much to discuss, such as homework, arithmetic, grammar, and most important, whether or not Harvey should go on to high school.

"Now that you're fifteen," Mr. Rothwell was saying, "you will soon be graduating from elementary school. You must make up your mind about high school."

Most young people did not go beyond elementary school. They worked on their fathers' farms or found jobs elsewhere.

136

"I'm going to be a trader," Harvey said. "I don't see why I should go on to high school. I know how to buy and sell horses now."

"That's true," Mr. Rothwell admitted, "and I've heard what a good trader you are. But do you think that you want to do that all your life, Harvey? What about the future?"

Harvey picked up a stone and skimmed it down the road. "I never thought about that," he said. "I don't know."

"It's just that you have too good a mind not to go on to school," Mr. Rothwell said. "With more education you could become a business-man and probably be very successful."

Harvey had thought only about trading horses. Once his cousin Clinton, who owned a large buggy factory in Columbus, had said he would be glad to have Harvey work for him. The job did not sound like as much fun as trading and Harvey had forgotten about it.

The next day was Saturday. At breakfast Mr. Firestone told Harvey that he wanted to sell two of his work horses. "Would you like to take them to the Salem Fair and see if you can sell them for me?" he asked.

"Of course!" Harvey exclaimed. "You know I like to trade horses. How much do you want me to get for them?"

Mr. Firestone thought for a moment. "I don't think they're worth more than fifteen dollars each. If you can get that I'll be satisfied, but if you can't find a buyer at that price, bring them back."

"I'll sell them," Harvey promised, and he lost no time tying them behind his buggy and setting off for the fair.

Mr. Dunbar was the first trader to come over and look at the horses. He wore the same dirty hat that he had worn before. He was soon joined by another trader whom everyone called

"Cheater." He was better dressed than Mr. Dunbar and had a large red nose.

"Those horses are no good, sonny," Mr. Dunbar said, shaking his head.

Cheater nodded his head. "Too old to do a day's work. Have to do better than that if you want to sell anything to us, boy."

Remembering his father's advice not to appear anxious to sell, Harvey shrugged his shoulders. "I don't have to sell them," he said. "But tell me, Mr. Dunbar, how much do you think they're really worth?"

Mr. Dunbar made a face. "No more than ten dollars—if you could find anyone who would give that much. Right, Cheater?"

The other man nodded without speaking, but Harvey noticed that he was still looking at the horses carefully.

"If that's the case," Harvey said, "I'll take them to another fair. They might bring a better price there anyway. No sense giving them away, is there?"

He watched Mr. Dunbar's face. He could tell that he was interested. There were not too many work horses for sale right now.

"I'll take another look, sonny," Mr. Dunbar said. "There's no sense in your having to go to all that bother."

"I don't mind," Harvey said. He wished Mr. Dunbar would stop calling him "sonny," but he did not dare tell him so.

A few minutes later Mr. Dunbar offered fifteen dollars for each horse, but Harvey shook his head.

"Twenty's my price," he said. "Take it or leave it."

Mr. Dunbar took off his hat and scratched his head. "You're quite a trader, aren't you, sonny? You know they aren't worth twenty or even fifteen dollars. But I'll tell you what. So

140

happens I need a couple of work horses bad. I'll split the difference and give you seventeen fifty. How's that?"

"Sold!" Harvey cried, delighted to have been able to get two dollars and a half more for each horse than his father had expected.

As Mr. Dunbar counted out the money Harvey wondered whether he might grow up to be a trader like Mr. Dunbar. Suddenly the business of horse trading lost its magic. He did not want to be doing this when he was an old man like Cheater. Already he was as good a trader as either of them, if not a better one. What fun would it be to spend the rest of his life doing this kind of work?

The following Monday afternoon he walked home with Mr. Rothwell after school and told him what he had decided.

"Do you think my folks will let me go to high school?" he asked the teacher. "Trading horses is all right, but I think I would like to do something better."

"I have no idea, Harvey," Mr. Rothwell replied. "Why don't you ask them? I have a feeling they'll be delighted."

After Mr. Firestone had said grace, Harvey took a long breath and asked, "Father, may I go to high school in the fall?"

Mr. Firestone speared a potato with his fork and chuckled quietly. Then he asked, "Why do you want to go to high school? I thought you were going to be a horse trader."

"I was," Harvey admitted, "but I can see that there's no future in that. With more education I should be able to get a better job."

"Oh, Harvey!" His mother pushed her chair back from the table and came over to kiss him. "We've so hoped you would want to go to high school, but we wanted you to make up your own mind. I'm so happy!"

"I am, too," his father said. "There's just one problem, though, Harvey. The high school is in town and that's a long trip. You could not drive back and forth every day through the snow or mud next winter."

"I think I know the answer."

All eyes turned toward Mrs. Firestone.

"Grandmother and Grandfather Flickinger are moving to town this summer," she said. "Aunt Nannie and her husband will live in the old home. Harvey could stay with his grandparents during the week and come home on weekends."

"Do you really think I could do that?" Harvey asked. His eyes shone. "And could I take Kitty with me—that is, if Grandfather and Grandmother have a barn?"

"They'll have a barn, never fear," his father said. "Grandfather Flickinger wouldn't be without horses."

144

Harvey explained that Mr. Rothwell was not sure that he was ready for high school. The course was to be lengthened from two to three years and would be more difficult.

"If you are willing to work hard this summer," Mr. Firestone said, "I'll pay for a tutor. Maybe Miss Snyder will help you. She's just been made principal of the high school."

"I'll work as hard as I can," Harvey promised. He was determined to amount to more in life than Mr. Dunbar or Cheater.

Life in Town

"HARVEY!" Grandfather Flickinger called. "Frank Roninger's downstairs. He wants to know whether you can go to the magic show at the Opera House with him."

Harvey came to the head of the stairs and waved to Frank.

"Thanks, but I've got to study tonight. Miss Snyder is giving us an important history test tomorrow. I want to do my best."

Frank snapped his fingers. "Maybe you're right, Harve," he said. "I need a good grade in that subject myself. I guess I'd better study, too."

146

Each night Harvey found that his high school subjects took a great deal of time to prepare. His studies had never been easy for him and now he had to work harder than ever. He was determined to graduate. He would let nothing keep him from earning that diploma!

Life was not all work, however. It was fun living with his grandparents. Grandmother Flickinger cooked his favorite foods and saw to it that he had a clean shirt each morning. His grandfather would try to help him with his homework whenever Harvey had trouble.

"I never had those newfangled subjects when I was a boy," his grandfather would say each time he was unable to answer one of Harvey's questions.

Every Friday afternoon after school Harvey hitched Kitty to his buggy, said good-bye to his grandparents, and drove home for the weekend. Sometimes he took George Cole, Frank Roninger, and other friends with him to enjoy one of his mother's famous chicken dinners.

"Welcome to the farm, boys," Mrs. Firestone would call as the buggy came to a stop. Then she would add quickly, "If you want dinner, you'll have to go get it yourselves."

The boys would hurry to the chicken yard, kill two or three chickens, and pluck and clean them. It seemed like no time at all before they sat down at the table to huge helpings of fried chicken, potatoes, carrots, homemade biscuits, and rich brown gravy.

Harvey had to return to town early Monday morning and would take a bale of hay for Kitty and a pie, cake, or preserves which Mrs. Firestone sent to her parents.

Each day after school Harvey enjoyed walking up Main Street to look at the store windows. He always stopped by the jewelry store, hoping that someone would enter the shop. There was

148

a sign on the door that read: *"Push Button, Then Enter."* This was to advertise a wonderful new electric bell, the first in town. Farther up the street he would pause outside the Opera House to read the notices telling about the concerts, lectures, plays, and other events that were presented there.

Sometimes he walked down to Union Street to look in the big buggy factory. Anything that moved on wheels interested him. Now that he was preparing for business, he often wondered what it would be like to work in such a place. Even though he had given up the idea of becoming a horse trader, he still liked to buy and sell more than anything else.

One day on his way back to the Flickingers' home Harvey met Will Esterly riding a new bicycle. It had a huge front wheel and a tiny back wheel. Will, who sat high up on a little seat, looked frightened.

149

"Hi, Harve," he called as he stopped the bike and slid off. "Want to try it?"

"Sure," Harvey replied, and lost no time climbing up on the seat as Will held the bicycle steady. Harvey started to pedal, but when Will let go the bike fell over sideways, throwing Harvey to the ground. He got to his feet, brushed the dust off his clothes, and climbed back up for another try.

"This thing is not going to lick me!" he told Will. This time he went faster and managed to keep the bicycle upright. It was fun riding along the road, but he had to steer around each stone or rut lest the front wheel hit it and throw him off. It was bumpy riding on the hard-packed dirt.

"Thanks, Will," he said when he returned to where his friend was standing. He jumped off and looked at the wheels for a moment. "You know, if the manufacturer put rubber over the

150

iron rims of those wheels, your bicycle would ride much better," he said.

"That's a good idea," Will agreed. "I wish bicycles were made that way. Do you want another ride, Harvey?"

"No, thanks," Harvey said, "but how about racing our horses down Main Street?" The boys often did this late in the afternoon.

"I'll get Judy and my rig and meet you in ten minutes," Will promised.

Harvey hurried to the barn, hitched Kitty to the little buggy, and soon the boys were speeding down the road. The horses were well matched and ran side by side.

"Come on, Kitty!" Harvey urged.

The horse liked to race and suddenly she increased her pace and pulled ahead of Will's horse. She beat Judy easily, and Harvey rewarded her with one of the sugar lumps he always carried in his pocket.

"That's some horse," Will said when he had caught up with Harvey. "I hope you'll bring her when we go to the Grand Army of the Republic picnic next Saturday."

"I'll see," was all that Harvey would say. He was not looking forward to the picnic because

all the girls and boys in his class would be there. He was still shy, especially around girls. It would be more fun if only the boys were going.

The next Friday Harvey did not drive home. On Saturday morning he hitched Kitty to his grandfather's buggy and drove over to the school grounds. He wore his Sunday clothes— a brown vest, a white collar, a white bow tie, a gold watch chain, and his best shirt.

"You'd better take an umbrella," his grandfather suggested as he was leaving. "It looks like rain and you're all dressed up." Harvey was no fonder of umbrellas than he was of girls and put it on the floor of the buggy.

The buggies all left from the school grounds, two couples to a carriage. Harvey and Ida sat on the front seat, George Cole and Harriet in the back. Harvey could not think of a single thing to say, but fortunately the two girls began to chat back and forth and did not seem to notice that the boys were tongue-tied.

"Everybody over here for the picture!" a photographer called shortly after the young people arrived at the picnic grounds. The girls and boys posed by a large cannon. The girls wore high-crowned hats and long full dresses. The boys, in their tight suits, looked older than their ages.

Once the pictures were taken everyone rushed over to the picnic tables where they found places already set. Plates heaped with fried chicken, roast corn, and tomatoes were eagerly eaten by the hungry young people.

"It's good," George said as he munched a big chicken leg, "but it's not half as good as your mother's, Harve."

Harvey smiled. It pleased him to hear his mother praised.

"I hear your mother is an excellent cook,"

Ida said. "Why don't you ask some of us girls out sometime?"

"Why, Ida!" Harriet gasped. "What a rude thing to say!"

Ida blushed and looked down at her plate. "I didn't mean to be rude, Harve," she said. "Please excuse me."

"That's all right," Harvey said, hoping to make her feel better. "Maybe we could arrange it sometime."

As they were finishing their ice cream and cake it started to rain. Harvey could see that there was no sense staying at the wet picnic ground and suggested leaving.

"I'll get the umbrella," he said, glad his grandfather had given it to him. "Wait here and I'll be right back."

As soon as everyone was in the carriage Harvey snapped the reins and Kitty started for Columbiana. The rain fell harder and harder until it turned to a downpour. The surface of the once-hard road began to soften. It became muddy and more and more slippery as they drove on. Finally they reached a little hill. Kitty started up it but kept slipping and could not pull the buggy any farther.

Harvey handed the reins to Ida. "You drive," he said. "I'll get out and push."

"I'll help," George said, and the two boys jumped down into the mud, which came up over their shoes.

"I wish I had two of these things," Harriet said, as she opened the umbrella and held it over Harvey.

"Thank you," he said, grateful for her kindness. "But be sure to give George a turn, too." He decided that maybe girls were all right.

With the boys' help Kitty was able to pull the buggy to the top of the hill. There George and Harvey jumped back in. They were very careful not to get mud on the girls' dresses. Kitty pulled the buggy back to town, but it was hard work all the way.

That night at dinner Harvey told his grandparents about the picnic and the trip home.

"I hope your clothes aren't ruined by that mud and water," his grandmother said. "I'll do my best to clean them and get them ironed for church tomorrow."

"Thank you," Harvey said. "I'm sorry to put you to so much trouble." He paused to wipe his mouth, then added, "You know, I have been thinking about that mud. There should be some way of fixing roads so they don't get muddy when it rains. If they were made of stone or something hard, we wouldn't have that trouble."

"That's true," his grandfather said. "Maybe when you get out into the business world you'll think of some way to do that."

"Maybe," Harvey said. "Just think, in three

weeks I'll graduate from high school and then I'll go out into the world!"

Thirteen young people graduated from the Columbiana High School that Friday night in May, 1887. Each member of the class gave a short talk and some offered musical selections. When the program was over the students gathered outdoors on the lawn to say good-bye.

As Harvey shook hands with Ida he had an idea. He whispered in her ear for a moment, after which she nodded her head eagerly.

"I think that would be just wonderful!" she said. Then Ida turned toward the others and called: "Quiet, everybody! Harve wants to tell you something!"

Harvey coughed and cleared his throat.

"I'm not going to make another speech," he said. "I just want to invite all of you to come out to the farm tomorrow night for one of my mother's chicken dinners."

158

The Young Businessman

HARVEY sat on a high stool in the dimly lit cellar of the Royal Coal and Mining Company in Columbus, Ohio. He was the bookkeeper who kept all of the coal company's accounts. The work was tiresome, the hours were long, and the pay was one dollar a day.

After graduation from high school Harvey had entered the Spencerian Business College in Cleveland to learn penmanship and bookkeeping. Once he finished those courses he planned to work for his cousin Clinton Firestone in his Columbus Buggy Works. It was a large company with sales offices in many cities. Cousin

Clinton found Harvey the bookkeeping position with the coal company because at that time he had no openings in his own factory.

A Mr. O. D. Jackson rented desk space in the room where Harvey worked. He owned a mine but spent all of his time reading newspapers and writing letters. He quickly discovered that Harvey was a careful worker and paid him ten dollars a month to keep his accounts. Harvey worked on them at night in his room and put the ten dollars in the savings bank.

Six months after Harvey had taken the bookkeeping job the Royal Coal and Mining Company failed. Harvey was out of work.

"Cheer up, young man," Mr. Jackson said when Harvey told him the news. "You can come to work for me. I'm going to make a line of patent medicines, lotions, and flavoring extracts for food. This is your chance to become rich!"

"But I don't want to be a bookkeeper any

longer," Harvey said. "It's boring work and I don't like it."

"Who said anything about bookkeeping?" Mr. Jackson asked. "You shall be one of my prize salesmen. You will travel around the state of Ohio selling my products."

"That's different," Harvey admitted. He had wanted to travel and see the world, and here was his chance. When he told his cousin about Mr. Jackson's offer, however, the buggy maker shook his head violently.

"Don't take that position," he advised. "Those patent medicines are probably no good and that man will go broke within a year. I'll give you a desk job in my factory."

Harvey thanked his cousin, but his mind was already made up. He hoped to make a lot of money. He was looking forward to traveling and liked the idea of being his own boss.

The first town he visited was Applecreek. He

walked into the lobby of the hotel and tried to avoid the looks of the older salesmen who were sitting there. After he left his suitcase in his room, he went out to see which stores would try his lotions and extracts.

There were two large drug stores near the hotel. Harvey walked by each but did not go in because he did not know what to say. Finally he went down a side street and found a small store. He took a deep breath, opened the door and made himself go in. Before he could open his sample case the man behind the counter said that he was not interested. Harvey tried another small store. The man there also told him that he did not want to see the samples. This made Harvey angry and he decided to go back to one of the large stores.

The owner was friendly, asked to see the samples and listened carefully as Harvey told him about each of the extracts.

"Smell this Wild Rose Lotion," Harvey suggested and passed the open bottle under the man's nose. "Isn't that good? It costs only a dollar and a half for a dozen bottles. Think of the profit you will make."

Before the man lost interest Harvey showed him a jug of Jackson's Flavoring Extract. "Let me pour a little on your finger. You can see for yourself how delicious it is," he said. "A gallon is only twelve dollars. You can resell it for five times that amount."

The storekeeper liked the taste and became Harvey's first customer.

In the other large store the young salesman was successful, too. There the owner bought lotions as well as extracts and was glad to have them. As he called on other stores, Harvey made more sales. He enjoyed what he was doing and was pleased to learn that he could sell things easily. His secret was to show the storekeeper how he, too, could make money with the lotions and extracts.

Harvey did not try to sell Mr. Jackson's medicines because he did not think that they would help people who were sick. He would never sell anything unless he was sure it was a good product. While he was traveling up and down the state of Ohio selling the lotions and extracts, Mr. Jackson's other salesmen were offering only the patent medicines. These older men did not try to sell the lotions and extracts. They thought that they would make more money handling the drugs.

They were wrong, though, because not enough people were willing to buy a new patent medicine. That was why Harvey was one of the few salesmen who were making sales and sending money into the company. Within six months after he had gone to work, he was the only salesman who was being paid by Mr. Jackson. Every

Monday morning his paycheck arrived at the hotel where he had stayed over the weekend.

One Monday when he was in Crestline the check did not arrive. It did not come Tuesday either, and by this time Harvey was out of money. He owed the hotel money, but he could not let the manager know he had no cash.

Every day he made believe that he was working, but he had already called on all the stores. Finally on Saturday the money arrived with a short note. "Dear Harvey: This is the last check I can send you. My company is broke. Good luck. O. D. Jackson."

Harvey returned to Columbus. He dreaded seeing his cousin, but he needed a job.

"You were right," he said. He stood in front of Clinton Firestone's desk and looked directly at him. "The company has failed. I'm out of work. If you have an opening where I could fit, I'd like to be considered for a job."

166

"I guess you've learned your lesson," Clinton said. "I'll give you a job in the shipping room where you'll be able to learn something about the business."

Although selling was Harvey's real interest, he was grateful for the chance to work. During lunch hour he would go up to the show room and watch the regular salesmen show the fancy carriages and buggies. He wanted to sell, too, but he was not given the opportunity.

Then there was trouble with the accounts in the Des Moines, Iowa, store. Clinton sent Harvey out there to help the bookkeeper. Next Harvey went to Detroit where his brother Elmer was the manager. Here, too, Harvey was put at a desk to keep the books, but he spent most of his time in the showroom.

One day Elmer came over to his desk. "How would you like to sell?" he asked.

Harvey grinned. "What do you think?"

"Starting tomorrow you can work in the show room. I've found a man to take your place."

Harvey had been selling for only a short time when Clinton decided to send Elmer to Des Moines. Robert, who had just graduated from Columbiana High School, went to Des Moines with his older brother. Harvey was put in charge of the company's Detroit office.

Now that he was a successful businessman, Harvey started parting his hair in the middle, grew a moustache and twirled both ends of it into points. He dressed well and traded horses until he had some of the best in town. Since he was selling buggies, he felt that he should always hitch the best horse to his carriage. Late afternoons and Saturdays he drove down Detroit's Grand Boulevard dressed in a derby hat, gloves, and fine clothes, with a lap robe pulled up over his knees.

One of the carriages in the showroom had

rubber-tired wheels. Harvey often took friends for a ride in this buggy because it rode so smoothly. Bicycles now had rubber tires filled with air, but Harvey's was the only carriage in the city with solid rubber tires.

From time to time he took an attractive young girl named Idabelle Smith for rides in this buggy. He had met her at a dancing party and courted her. They became engaged and were married in November, 1895. Nothing was too good for his bride, Harvey thought.

He took her to Washington and New York, where he spent all his savings on their honeymoon. When they returned to Detroit Harvey found that buggy sales had dropped alarmingly. Now no one would pay forty dollars extra for a set of solid rubber-tired wheels.

One day a tall lanky young man with bright eyes came into the show room.

"I've just built a gasoline-driven horseless

carriage," he said. "It's too heavy to use on bicycle wheels with their thin rubber tires. What do you have?"

Harvey showed him a new set of wheels with solid rubber tires that had just come from the factory. The man examined them carefully for some time.

"I'll take them," he said at last. "Send them over to Bagley Avenue, please. The name is Henry Ford."

Meanwhile business throughout the country became bad and people stopped buying the Columbus Buggies because they were too expensive. Early in 1896 the company failed. Elmer and Robert returned to the farm in Columbiana. Harvey did not think it would be right to take his new wife back home and ask his father to support them.

"Well, Idabelle," he said, when he told her the news, "this is the third time the company I worked for failed. Only difference is that now I have a wife and no savings and business everywhere is bad, but we'll manage. Somehow I'm going to go into business for myself— there's a great future in rubber—and I intend to succeed!"

Idabelle put her arm around him, looked up into his face, and smiled.

"I'm sure you will, Harvey," she said, "and I'll help all I can."

Success at Last

"SOMEDAY every buggy in America will have rubber tires," Harvey said one day to a man whom he knew in Detroit. "And I intend to help make it happen!" The man liked Harvey and agreed to put some money into a new tire company. Another businessman whom Harvey knew said that he, too, would become a partner with Harvey and his friend in the new company.

As soon as Harvey could borrow some money he and Idabelle moved to Chicago, Illinois. There he had learned that the Victor Rubber Tire Company, which made bicycle tires, wanted to sell its shop. Harvey bought the

172

business with all its tools and started the Firestone-Victor Rubber Tire Company.

Next he hired a blacksmith. The blacksmith's job would be to take the steel rims off carriage wheels. Then he would hammer on new metal rims and clamp a piece of rubber to them.

Harvey drove throughout the city in a wagon looking for business. He called on stables that kept carriages and on all the undertakers. At first there was little interest. Idabelle tried to keep their weekly bill for food to five dollars or less. Then things changed.

Articles in newspapers told that President William McKinley had bought three carriages for the White House. All of them had rubber tires. Suddenly people wanted rubber tires on their carriages, too, and Harvey's business began to boom. The Firestone-Victor Rubber Tire Company grew rapidly, and in 1899 Harvey's two partners bought him out at a handsome profit. Now he was free to move to Akron, Ohio. Akron, which was only fifty miles from his father's farm, was known as the Rubber City.

It was a snowy January day when the Harvey Firestone family arrived in Akron. Mr. and Mrs. Firestone walked from the railroad station to the Windsor Hotel. Mr. Firestone held their new baby, Harvey Firestone, Jr., with one arm and lugged the suitcase with his other hand. Mrs. Firestone carried her pocketbook and a bag filled with the baby's clothing. A few days later they found an apartment, and then Mr. Firestone was ready for the long and hard task of starting his own business.

On August 3, 1900, the Firestone Tire and Rubber Company was founded. The office and shop were in a one-room building in Akron. Elmer, who was out of a job, came to work as a clerk and stayed for a short time. Before long

Harvey sent Robert to open an office for the new company in Chicago.

For the first two years Mr. Firestone bought tires from another company and resold them to his customers. Late in 1902 he purchased a one-story building and some second-hand machinery so that he could make his own tires. At the same time he hired ten men to work for him.

The whole family came out to the factory for the grand opening. Mrs. Firestone was there holding Russell, their second baby. The new workers also were on hand for the big event. Mr. Firestone lifted Harvey, Jr., and placed his hand on the valve of the big engine.

"Now pull!" Mr. Firestone said. The little boy pulled the valve and the flywheel on the old engine began to turn.

"Hurrah!" everyone shouted.

"We may have second-hand machinery," Mr. Firestone said, "but we have first-class men."

It was not long before "horseless carriages" were widely used. Solid rubber tires, however, did not give a comfortable ride. For easy riding these new automobiles needed pneumatic tires like those used on bicycles. A group of companies owned all the rights to make a clincher pneumatic tire. This tire required hooks to keep it on the wheel rim. Although the association permitted its members to make clincher tires, it refused to give Mr. Firestone a license to make this kind of tire.

"All right," Mr. Firestone told his foreman, when he heard the news, "we'll invent a different type of pneumatic tire." He did so and when he tested it and found that it worked well, he called on his friend Henry Ford, who was now making automobiles. Mr. Firestone had heard that Mr. Ford was about to buy a large number of tires for his new cars.

"I have a new kind of tire," Mr. Firestone

told his friend. "The people who buy your cars will like it. The price is right and it will help you make a larger profit on each car you sell." Then he explained all the advantages of his new invention.

Mr. Ford listened carefully. When Mr. Firestone had finished talking, the automobile maker leaned back in his chair.

"I know all about your tires and they are good," he said. "I'll take two thousand. How is that for an order?"

Two thousand tires! Nobody had ever ordered that many tires at one time. Mr. Firestone could hardly wait until he got home to tell his wife. Everything was going beautifully now. The company was doing more than a million dollars' worth of business a year. It had acquired a three-story factory, and now he had a huge order from Henry Ford.

Just as the first shipment of tires left the plant

for Ford's factory in Detroit, Mr. Firestone received a telegram saying that he must stop production at once. Mr. Ford had decided that buyers of his cars would not be able to find garage men who knew how to repair the Firestone tires. He was afraid that the public would stop buying his cars.

Mr. Firestone hurried to Detroit to talk with Mr. Ford.

"You will have to make the clincher tires," Mr. Ford said.

"But I can't!" Mr. Firestone protested. "Don't you understand? The association that owns the patents won't let me make them."

"Bah!" Mr. Ford waved his hand. "They can't stop you from making them. My lawyers have looked into the matter. What the association is doing is not legal."

"I hope that is the case," Mr. Firestone said. "I'll see what I can do." He wanted to keep the order, but he was not sure that Mr. Ford's lawyers were right.

That night he took the train to New York. The next morning he went directly to the offices of the association that owned the patents on the clincher tire. His heart was racing as he asked to see the president of the association. He had to get that Ford order.

"What do you want with us, Mr. Firestone?" the president asked.

Mr. Firestone explained why he had come. Then he said, "If you do not give me a license so that I can make clincher tires, too, I will go ahead and make them without one and I won't pay you a penny."

"And I will bring you to court!" the president said as he pounded his fist on his desk. "Good day, Mr. Firestone."

As soon as he returned to Akron, Mr. Firestone went to his lawyer's office. The lawyer told him to make all the clincher tires he could sell. Thereupon the little factory made the two thousand tires for Ford. The president of the tire association sued the Firestone Company, but a judge ruled that Mr. Firestone could make clinchers without a license and without paying any fees.

As the years went by Mr. Firestone sold more and more tires and the company became prosperous. One thing bothered him, however, about the tires that were being made then. They were too smooth and often slipped and skidded when roads were wet. He molded a tread on his tires which had raised letters in two lines that read:

FIRESTONE NON-SKID

The new tread made driving safer.

In 1911 Mr. Firestone opened a new factory south of Akron. It was made of yellow brick and had four stories with four wings at each end of the main building. In front there was a broad green lawn.

At the same time the tire maker built a new home for his family in West Akron. He called it Harbel Manor, using part of his and his wife's first names for Harbel. The Firestones needed a large house.

Harvey, Jr., and Russell now had two more brothers, Raymond and Leonard. Soon a fifth son, Roger, was born, and a daughter, Elizabeth, was born two years after the family moved into Harbel Manor. The Firestone family was complete.

Making a
Better World

THE IDEA of an annual outing was born in 1915 at the Panama-Pacific Exposition in San Francisco. It was Edison Day at the Exposition, and the white-haired inventor had come in his private railroad car from Orange, New Jersey. On the way he had picked up Luther Burbank, the famous botanist. At the station in San Francisco, Henry Ford and Harvey Firestone were waiting to meet the inventor and his friend.

That afternoon Mr. Firestone could see that all the speeches, parades, and confusion had tired Mr. Edison.

"Why don't you and Mrs. Edison come for a

little drive with Idabelle and me?" Mr. Firestone suggested. The Edisons accepted the invitation quickly and the two couples rode away from the busy city.

"It would be fun to take a long drive sometime," Mr. Edison said as they drove along the coast of the Pacific Ocean. "I never seem to have much time to take it easy."

The next day Mr. Burbank invited the Edisons, Firestones, and Fords to visit his home at nearby Santa Rosa and see his experimental farm. He was growing peas for a canning company. All of the peas were the same size and ripened at the same time. After seeing the farm, the three couples said good-bye to Mr. Burbank and drove to San Diego along the new highway. After celebrating another Edison Day there, the friends were ready to go home.

"Before we leave one another," Mr. Edison said, "I want to invite you gentlemen to make a gypsy trip by car next summer. I will name the date, choose the route, and make the rules. How about it?"

Mr. Firestone and Mr. Ford thought it was a fine idea.

The following summer Mr. Firestone and Harvey, Jr., drove to Orange, New Jersey. They took several helpers with them as well as a truck that carried a refrigerator and food. Mr. Edison provided another truck which was loaded with tents, tables and chairs, electric batteries and lights. Mr. Ford arrived, bringing Sata, his Japanese cook.

On their way they picked up eighty-year-old John Burroughs, the well-known naturalist. He looked like a saint, with his sad eyes and his flowing white beard. He took an immediate liking to Harvey, Jr.

As the party drove up through New York State, Mr. Edison avoided the busy highways

and chose bumpy dirt roads instead. The friends camped at night in fields. After dinner they sat around the campfire talking and joking. Mr. Edison, Mr. Firestone, and Mr. Ford would go to bed early, but Harvey, Jr., and Mr. Burroughs sat up talking until late.

The next year, 1917, America was at war and the men were too busy to plan another trip. The following summer they were all tired from working long hours and needed a change. Although the war was not yet over, they met in Pittsburgh for a trip through the Blue Ridge and Smoky Mountains. The year after that they toured New England states.

These annual camping trips provided good stories for newspapers. People everywhere read about the famous men. In 1921 President Warren G. Harding joined the group. He came with a secretary, six Secret Service men, nine movie men and ten newspaper reporters.

Was it the bumpy rides Mr. Firestone took with his friends over the dirt roads, or was it that he still remembered pushing the buggy through mud when he was a young man and driving Kitty? Whatever the reason, he knew that America needed better highways for its growing number of automobiles and trucks.

"Automobiles and trucks will never become useful until there are good roads," he said.

In 1920 he made numerous speeches before business organizations and civic clubs urging people to demand better highways. He explained that if trucks could travel over smooth hard surfaces it would be possible for factories to ship their goods to stores all over the country. This would bring greater prosperity.

At his direction the Firestone Company held an essay contest for high school students. The subject was good roads and the prize was a four-year college education, all expenses paid.

The first year of the contest more than 200,000 students mailed essays to the judges. President Harding awarded the first prize to an Idaho girl. Mr. Firestone continued the contest for five years and gradually the American people awakened to the need for good highways. By 1925 America was spending almost a billion dollars on its roads each year.

Mr. Firestone thought that better roads called for better tires. He was certain that the pneumatic tire, which was packed tightly with air, could be improved.

"Let's see if we can make tires larger and fill them with less air," he told his chief engineer one day. "I think such tires will give a more comfortable ride."

The Firestone Company engineers and chemists went to work on the idea. In 1923 the company started making a brand-new tire which it called the air-cushion tire. It was larger than the narrow tires in use at that time and it looked something like a balloon.

Almost overnight this became known as a balloon tire. At first Mr. Ford and other makers of automobiles were afraid that the balloon tires would be unsafe. After Mr. Firestone showed that this was not true, the automobile companies began to use the balloon tires and they are still being made.

As the five Firestone sons grew older they helped their father run the business, leaving him free to spend more time on the family farm near Columbiana. He enjoyed cutting and mowing the hay, looking after the horses, and doing odd jobs about the farm. When cold weather came he and Mrs. Firestone went south and spent the winter months at their Florida estate, which they called Harbel Villa.

On Sunday, February 6, 1938, Mr. Firestone went to church with Russell and then enter-

190

tained friends for dinner. In the afternoon he went to the stables, hitched his favorite horse to a buggy, and took a short drive. After a supper of crackers and milk he did not feel well and decided to go to bed early. He died in his sleep that night.

His sons, Harvey, Jr., Russell, Leonard, Raymond, and Roger, continued active in managing the business. By the 1960's the business he had started in a one-room building had grown until it was operating factories all over the world. Besides turning out tires the Firestone Company was now making plastics, textiles, chemicals, metal products, home, garden, and automotive supplies, and a great variety of other things.

After Mr. Firestone's death his sons set up the old homestead in Columbiana as a model farm, just as their father would have wanted. Today, the Firestone Homestead Farms are known not only for their fine beef cattle and excellent crops but also for their soil conservation research, and forestry studies.

Young and old who are interested in farming may visit the farms. They can also see the red brick farmhouse which still stands exactly as it was when Harvey Firestone and his family lived in it.

More About This Book

WHEN HARVEY S. FIRESTONE LIVED

1868 HARVEY S. FIRESTONE WAS BORN NEAR COLUMBIANA, OHIO, DECEMBER 20.

There were 37 states in the Union.

Andrew Johnson was President.

The population of the country was about 38,560,000.

1868– HARVEY GREW UP ON THE FAMILY FARM NEAR
1887   COLUMBIANA AND ATTENDED SCHOOL.

The first transcontinental railroad was completed, 1869.

Alexander Graham Bell invented and demonstrated the telephone, 1876.

Bicycles were first manufactured in this country, 1878.

Thomas Edison invented the phonograph, 1878, and the electric light bulb, 1879.

The Civil Service System was begun, 1883.

The first electric street railway in the United States was operated in Batimore, 1885.

1887– YOUNG FIRESTONE HELD SEVERAL JOBS AND BE-
1900   CAME INTERESTED IN RUBBER TIRES.

Thomas Edison invented the moving-picture camera, 1889.

Henry Ford built his first gas engine, 1893, and his first automobile, 1896.

The Spanish-American War was fought, 1898.

1900– FIRESTONE FOUNDED AND DIRECTED THE FIRE-
1920   STONE TIRE AND RUBBER COMPANY.

Wilbur and Orville Wright flew the first heavier-than-air aircraft, 1903.

Robert Peary discovered the North Pole, 1909.

The Panama Canal was completed and opened to world traffic, 1914.

World War I was fought, 1914-1918.

1920– FIRESTONE PIONEERED IN DEVELOPING AND
1938   MANUFACTURING IMPROVED TYPES OF TIRES.

The League of Nations was formed, 1920.

Stock market prices crashed and a severe business depression followed, 1929.

Wiley Post flew a small airplane around the world, 1933.

194

1938   HARVEY S. FIRESTONE DIED IN MIAMI BEACH,
FLORIDA, FEBRUARY 7.

There were forty-eight states in the Union.

Franklin D. Roosevelt was President.

The population of the country was about
129,680,000.

DO YOU REMEMBER?

1. What became of the cookies Harvey was supposed to take to the neighbor lady?

2. How did Harvey finally get his mother's chickens back in their pen?

3. How did Harvey and George keep King from following them while they were coasting?

4. How did King embarrass Harvey on the first day of school?

5. How did Harvey happen to lose Robert one evening at the fair?

6. Why was Harvey disappointed when he tried to grow and sell vegetables?

7. How did Harvey and Pete free the cat trapped in the stone wall?

8. What offer did a drummer make to Harvey one day at the railroad station?

9. Why did Mr. Firestone give Harvey a horse of his own on the farm?

10. How did Harvey have an opportunity to attend high school in Columbiana?

11. How did young Firestone spend the first few years after he graduated?

12. How did Firestone get started in the rubber tire industry?

13. How did Firestone achieve success through the Firestone Tire and Rubber Company?

14. What famous friends frequently joined Firestone on outings in his later years?

IT'S FUN TO LOOK UP THESE THINGS

1. What horse-drawn vehicles were widely used when Firestone was a boy?

2. When did rubber tires first come into use on bicycles and horse-drawn carriages?

3. What were some of the most popular early automobiles built in America?

4. How did the coming of automobiles lead to the improvement of highways?

5. Why did Akron, Ohio, become known as "the rubber capital" of the country?

6. Who were some of the American pioneers in the rubber industry besides Firestone?

INTERESTING THINGS YOU CAN DO

1. Find out where most of the large rubber plantations in the world are located.

2. Prepare a report to explain the process of vulcanizing rubber.

3. Explain some of the advantages of inflated tires over solid rubber tires.

4. Collect pictures to show what tires were like on some of the first automobiles.

5. Draw a map to show where Akron, Ohio, "the rubber capital" is located.

6. Make a list of different kinds of modern vehicles that use rubber tires.

7. Name important products besides tires that are made wholly or partially from rubber.

OTHER BOOKS YOU MAY ENJOY READING

Early Days of Automobiles, Elizabeth Janeway. Random House.

Henry Ford: Boy with Ideas, Hazel B. Aird and Catherine Ruddiman. Trade and School Editions, Bobbs-Merrill.

John Burroughs: Boy of Field and Stream, Lucy Post Frisbee. Trade and School Editions, Bobbs-Merrill.

Magic of Rubber, The, E. Joseph Dreany. Putnam.

Ohio: From Its Glorious Past to the Present, Alan Carpenter. Childrens Press.

Picture Book of Ohio, Bernardine Bailey. Whitman.

Tom Edison: Boy Inventor, Sue Guthridge. Trade and School Editions, Bobbs-Merrill.

INTERESTING WORDS IN THIS BOOK

burlap (bûr′lăp) : heavy, coarse fabric made from hemp or jute and used for wrappings

chore (chōr) : daily work regularly done about a farm or house

clenched (klĕncht) : closed tightly together, as the hands or teeth

clincher (klĭn'chēr): automobile tire with flanges to fit into the wheel rim

coop (ko͞op): small building used for sheltering poultry

crop (krŏp): handle of a riding whip with a loop in the end for opening gates

derby (dûr'bĭ): stiff felt hat with a dome-shaped crown and a narrow brim

diploma (dĭ plō'mȧ): official document given a person graduating from a high school or college

dreaded (drĕd'ĕd): felt reluctant to meet someone or to take some action

drummer (drŭm'ēr): person who travels from town to town selling goods

embarrassed (ĕm băr'ȧst): made to feel self-conscious or ill at ease

extracts (ĕks'trăkts): concentrated substances from leaves, blossoms, and other parts of plants

flywheel (flī' hwēl'): heavy wheel that regulates the speed of certain machines

gobbled (gŏb' 'ld): gulped or ate hastily

jounce (jouns): bounce or move in an up-and-down manner

muttered (mŭt'ērd): grumbled or spoke in a low voice with lips partly closed

neigh (nā) : horse's long, loud cry

patent medicine (păt'ĕnt) : packaged medicine drug protected by a trademark that may be purchased without a doctor's prescription

pneumatic (nŭ măt'ĭk) : filled with compressed air

promptly (prŏmpt'lē) : punctually

reduce (rē̇ dūs') : lower, as a price

responsibility (rē̇ spŏn'sĭ bĭl'ĭ tĭ) : something for which a person is accountable

saddle soap (săd'l sōp) : mild soap used for conditioning and cleaning leather

shied (shīd) : jumped to one side suddenly in fright or alarm

shoo (sho͞o) : scare or drive animals away, as by shouting or yelling

soapstone (sōp'stōn') : kind of soft stone greasy or soapy to touch

tread (trĕd) : raised or thickened part of a tire that comes in contact with a road

trembled (trĕm'b'ld) : shook involuntarily

valve (vălv) : device that controls the flow of a liquid or gas

wicker (wĭk'ēr) : small pliant twig, usually of willow, used in making baskets and chairs

wiry (wīr'ĭ) : lean and vigorous, sinewy

200

Childhood
OF FAMOUS AMERICANS

CHILDHOOD OF FAMOUS AMERICANS